In the Realms
of Mediumship

Francisco Candido Xavier

In the Realms of Mediumship

Life in the Spirit World

Dictated by the spirit
Andre Luiz

Acknowledgement
*The translators would like to thank the United States Spiritist Medical
Association for their help with the medical terms in this book.*

ISBN: 978-85-7945-429-5

Original title in Portuguese:
NOS DOMÍNIOS DA MEDIUNIDADE
Brazil, 1955

Translated by: Darrel W. Kimble and Ily Reis
Cover design by: Luciano Carneiro Holanda and Evelyn Yuri Furuta
Layout: Ingrid Saori Furuta
Photo: www.istockphoto.com/ AVTG

Edition of
INTERNATIONAL SPIRITIST COUNCIL
SGAN Q. 909 – Conjunto F
70790-090 – Brasilia (DF) – Brazil
www.edicei.com
edicei@edicei.com
+55 61 3038-8400
Sales: + 55 61 3038 8425

First Edition 9/2011

Authorized edition by Brazilian Spiritist Federation

INTERNATIONAL DATA FOR CATALOGING IN PUBLICATION (ICP)

L979a Luiz, André (Spirit)
     In the Realms of Mediumship / by the Spirit Andre Luiz ; [received by] Francisco Cândido Xavier ; [translated by Darrel W. Kimble and Ily Reis]. - Brasilia, DF (Brazil) : International Spiritist Council, 2011.
     264 p. ; 21 cm

     Translated from: Nos Domínios da Mediunidade
     ISBN 978-85-7945-429-5

     1. Spiritist Novel. 2. Spiritism. 3. Psychographic Works. I. Xavier, Francisco Cândido, 1910-2002. II. International Spiritist Council. III. Title. IV. Series.

                         CDD: 133.93
                         CDU: 133.7

Contents

Rays, Waves, Mediums, Minds... 7

1 – Studying Mediumship 11
2 – The Psychoscope 19
3 – The Mediumistic Team 27
4 – At Work 35
5 – The Assimilation of Mental Currents 43
6 – Conscious Psychophony 51
7 – Spiritual Rescue 59
8 – Somnambulistic Psychophony 67
9 – Possession 75
10 – Tormented Somnambulism 83
11 – An Out-of-Body Task 93
12 – Clairvoyance and Clairaudience 101
13 – Thought and Mediumship 109
14 – In Spiritual Service 117
15 – Corrupted Abilities 125
16 – The Mediumistic Mandate 135
17 – The Service of Passes 149
18 – Side Notes 159
19 – Telepathic Domination 167
20 – Mediumship and Prayer 175
21 – Mediumship on the Death Bed 185
22 – Emerging from the Past 193

23 – Fascination 201

24 – Expiatory Struggle 209

25 – Mental Fixation 217

26 – Psychometry 223

27 – Mediumship Gone Astray 231

28 – Physical Effects 237

29 – Annotations about the Work 251

30 – Closing Pages 259

Rays, Waves, Mediums, Minds...

In studying the composition of matter, 20th century science has gone from surprise to surprise, causing it to revise long-held beliefs.

Almost five centuries before Christ, Democritus's teacher, Leucippus, theorized that everything was composed of infinitesimal particles (atoms) that were in constant motion. But in spite of this, classical culture continued to be based on the four principles of Aristotelian thought – water, earth, air and fire – or on the three hypostatical elements of the ancient alchemists – sulfur, salt and mercury – in order to explain the many combinations in the physical world.

In the 19th century, Dalton scientifically proposes the corpuscular theory of matter, and highly respectable scholars begin an extraordinary period of investigation, renewing ideas and concepts based on the so-called "indivisible particle."

Extraordinary discoveries open up new and grand horizons to human knowledge.

Crookes discovers the radiant state of matter and studies cathode rays.

Röntgen observes that invisible radiations pass through a Crookes tube wrapped in black cardboard and discovers X-rays.

Henri Becquerel, allured by the subject, experiments with uranium while looking for radiations of the same grade and finds cause for further research.

The Curies, intrigued by this enigma, analyze tons of pitchblende and discover radium.

Old scientific affirmations tremble on their foundations.

Rutherford, at the forefront of a large group of pioneers, begins prominent studies involving radioactivity.

The atom experiences an irresistible attack against the fortress in which it is hiding and entrusts to humankind the solution to numerous secrets.

Ever since the last quarter of the 19th century, the earth has become a kingdom of waves and rays, currents and vibrations.

Everything pulsates with electricity and magnetism, movement and attraction.

The study of cosmic rays has demonstrated the fantastic energies scattered throughout the universe, providing physicists with a powerful instrument for investigating atomic and sub-atomic phenomena.

Bohrs, Planck and Einstein construct new and grand concepts.

The vehicle of flesh, the human body, is now nothing more than an electric vortex governed by consciousness.

Each tangible body is a bundle of concentrated energy. Matter is transformed into energy, and energy disappears to give way to matter.

Raised to the status of investigators of the truth, chemists and physicists, geometricians and mathematicians have become today's priests of the spirit without desiring it. Due to their ongoing studies, materialism and atheism will be compelled to vanish for lack of matter, the base that had ensured their negativistic speculations.

Laboratories are temples in which intelligence is driven to serve God; and even when intellectual activity is misguided, temporarily subordinated to the political hegemony that generates wars, the progress of science as a divine conquest continues to exalt the good and is bound for a glorious future.

That future belongs to the spirit!

Meditating on the future of the earthly community, Andre Luiz has written these few pages regarding mediumship, understanding the growing importance of the spiritual interchange between individuals.

The farther the evolutionary ascent, the more assuredly humans perceive the non-existence of death as the cessation of life.

Now, more than ever, people see themselves as consciousnesses held amid forces and fluids that are temporarily combined for educational purposes.

They are slowly starting to grasp the fact that the grave is the door to renewal, just as the cradle is the access to the human experience, and they realize that their stay on the planet is a journey with a destiny aimed at the stages of Greater Progress.

On this great pilgrimage, we are all instruments of the forces with which we are in tune. We are all mediums within our own mental field, associating ourselves with edifying energies when our thoughts flow towards the higher life or with disturbing and depressing forces as long as we are still enslaved to the shadows of a primeval and tormented life.

Through the sentiments that characterize their inner life, all individuals emit specific rays and live within the spiritual wave with which they identify themselves.

Such truths cannot remain semi-hidden in our sanctuaries of faith; they will radiate from the temples of science like mathematical equations.

And while various learners focus on mediumship, studying it from earth to heaven, our friend Andre, taking part in building a new age, has tried to analyze its position and character from heaven to earth.

However, what we want to emphasize in his account is the need to keep Christ in our hearts and minds in order not to become disoriented upon coming in contact with mediumistic phenomena.

Without the notion of responsibility, without devotion to the practice of the good, without the love of studying and without a persevering effort in our own personal moral education, the liberating pilgrimage toward the Higher Life is impossible.

Andre Luiz is clear enough; we do not have to expand on further considerations.

To each medium, his or her own mind.

To each mind, its own rays, personalizing observations and interpretations.

According to the rays we emit, our own spiritual dwelling will rise within the wave of thoughts preferred by our souls.

In essence, it is the same as repeating with Jesus:

"To each according to his deeds."

Emmanuel
Pedro Leopoldo, October 3, 1954

1
Studying Mediumship

"Undoubtedly," agreed Assistant Aulus, "mediumship is one of the most intriguing issues in the world today. Human beings are approaching the Era of the Spirit under the light of the Cosmic Religion of Love and Wisdom, and they will certainly need assistance in order to understand it."

At Minister Clarencio's request, this instructor, with his amiable and noble countenance, had just welcomed us for a brief course on mediumistic science.

Aulus specialized in activities of this nature and had dedicated many selfless years to them; thus, out of all the relationships of Minister Clarencio – our sponsor and advisor – he was one of the most competent instructors on the topic.

Aulus had welcomed us affably and kindly.

As he spoke about the questions afflicting humankind, he fixed his firm and lucid gaze on us not only with the interest of an older brother, but also with the affection of a tender father.

Hilario and I could hardly disguise our admiration.

It was a privilege to hear him discuss the topic that had brought us to him.

He was a combination of a rich core of knowledge and the deepest sentiment of love. We were delighted as we listened to him talk about human needs with the warmth of a benevolent and wise doctor who becomes an ordinary nurse for the sheer joy of helping and saving others.

Aulus had been interested in mediumistic experiments since 1779, when he had known Mesmer in Paris while studying the celebrated propositions introduced to the public by the famous magnetizer. He had reincarnated again at the beginning of the 19th century and witnessed firsthand the accomplishments of Allan Kardec in the codification of Spiritism. He was close to Cahagnet, Balzac, Theophile Gautier and Victor Hugo, ending his days in France after several decades dedicated to mediumship and magnetism in the scientific molds of Europe. In the spirit world, he had proceeded along the same lines, observing and working in his educational apostolate. Having dedicated himself for over thirty years to the task of spiritualization in Brazil, Aulus commented optimistically on the hopes of this new arena of action as he shared with us his exquisite trove of memories and experiences.

We were so enthralled as we listened to him that we could barely respond to his questions.

"Yes, we are familiar with some aspects of spirit interchange," I respectfully replied at a given moment. "Our desire, however, is to get a broader idea of the subject as simply as possible. On other occasions we made a cursory study of a few phenomena such as psychography[1], incorporation[2] and

---

[1] The reception of written spirit messages through a medium. – Tr.

[2] Although this expression is still used for oral spirit communications (psychophony would be the appropriate term), *Incorporation* (mediumistic spirit communication), if taken literally, would be a misleading term – two spirits (the medium's own spirit and the communicating spirit) cannot "inhabit" the same body. The communicating entity

materialization, but our study has been quite limited in light of the multiple services with which mediumship is endowed.

Our host kindly assented to enlightening us.

He was working in several departments and would lavish on us what he humbly considered as "a few notes."

To start with, Aulus invited us to listen to a friend who was going to speak about mediumship to a small group of incarnate and discarnate students, and whose words he considered opportune and valuable.

He didn't have to make his kindly offer twice, and with no time to lose, we quickly followed him.

In a large hall at the Ministry of Communications, we were introduced to Instructor Alberio, who was about to start his lecture.

We sat down among dozens of others in attentive and silent expectation.

As with so many other instructors whom I knew, Alberio approached the lectern with simplicity, as if he were merely a brother conversing with us in a fraternal manner.

"My friends," he said with assurance, "in continuation of our previous studies, we need to consider the fact that the mind is the basis for all mediumistic phenomena.

"We realize that the universe, which extends into the infinite with millions and millions of suns, is the externalization of Divine Thought, whose essence we share in our condition of conscious rays of the Eternal Wisdom within the limitations of spiritual evolution.

"From the superstructure of the heavenly bodies to the infrastructure of the sub-atomic world, everything is immersed

---

connects to the medium's mind and transmits its thoughts and commands, which a disciplined medium can either accept or reject. In cases of subjugation, spirits can control the subject's body, but it is still a mind-to-mind process, as they cannot expel the incarnate spirit from its body to make it their own. – Tr.

in the living substance of the Mind of God, just as fish and aquatic plants are immersed in the immense ocean.

"As children of the Creator, we have inherited from Him the faculty of creating, developing, nurturing and transforming.

"Naturally circumscribed within the conceptual dimensions in which we find ourselves, and in spite of the insignificance of our position when compared to the glory of the spirits who have already reached the angelic state, we can radiate the active energy of our own thoughts, thereby establishing around our own individuality the psychic atmosphere that is particular to each one of us.

"Each world possesses its own electromagnetic field tensor at the level of the gravitational force in which it is balanced. Similarly, each soul is enveloped within the sphere of the living forces that emerge from its mental 'breath' within the circle of individuals it is drawn to according to its need either to make adjustments or to grow spiritually towards immortality.

"Each planet revolves within the orbit assigned to it by the laws of equilibrium but without exceeding its own lines of gravitation, just as each consciousness evolves in the spiritual group to whose activities it has subordinated itself.

"So, we comprise a vast group of intelligences that are attuned to the same vibratory pattern of perception. We are part of a Whole made up of billions of beings that form, so to speak, earthly humankind.

"Thus, as only a humble family in the infinite concert of cosmic life, in which each world harbors only one specific family of Universal Humanity, we know for the time being merely those expressions of life that most closely speak to us, limited as we are to the degree of knowledge we have acquired so far.

"Depending on our fellow beings on our trajectory towards the evolutionary vanguard, we act and react upon one another –

just as the worlds that move through space are influenced by the heavenly bodies that surround them – by means of the mental energy in which we constantly renew ourselves, creating, feeding and destroying forms and situations, landscapes and things in the structuring of our own destinies.

"Our mind is thus a nucleus of intelligent forces that generates a subtle plasma, which, because we are constantly emitting it, offers objective resources to the images of our imagination under the command of our own designs.

"The idea is a 'being' organized by our spirit, to which thought gives form and upon which our will impresses movement and direction.

"Our very existence is a result of the sum of our ideas."

The lecturer took a brief pause that no one dared to interrupt, and then proceeded:

"As is easy to deduce, all living beings breathe within the dynamic psychic wavelength that is peculiar to them, within the dimensions that are characteristic of them, or within the frequency that is proper for them. This psychic process is independent of the central nervous system, because, since it flows from the mind, it is the process that conditions all the phenomena of organic life.

"Thus, examining the soul's characteristics as faculties of communication between spirits on whatever plane they may be, we cannot lose sight of the agent's or receiver's mental world, since, in any mediumistic situation, the receiver's intelligence is subject to the possibilities and thought nuances in which it lives. The sender's intelligence is likewise subject to the limits and interpretations of the thoughts it is capable of producing.

"Discarnate primitives communicating with learned incarnates will not be able to offer them any more information than the banal subjects concerning their experiences as primitives. Conversely, when communicating with primitives still attached to their primitive habitat, learned discarnates will not be able to offer them their immediate assistance, except in a very narrow circle in which their mental interests are imbedded, such as helping them with a herd of cattle or in curing an illness of the material body. That is why primitives would not feel comfortable in the company of learned persons and learned persons, in turn, would not keep company with primitives for lack of that almost imponderable nourishment which we could classify as 'compensatory vibrations'.

"It is a law that our greatest joys result from contact with those who understand us and exchange with us mental values similar to our own, just as trees offer a greater coefficient of production if situated among others of the same species with which they exchange their germinating principles.

"In mediumship, therefore, we cannot overlook the issue of attunement.

"We attract spirits who are attuned to us as much as we are attuned to them. And if it is true that each one of us can only give according to what he or she has, it is unquestionable that each one receives according to what he or she gives.

"Since the mind is the basis for all mediumistic manifestations in whatever ways they are expressed, it is crucial that we enrich our thought with moral and cultural treasures because they are the only treasures that make it possible to fixate the light that descends upon us from the Highest Realms through the spirits of wisdom and love who oversee our lives.

"Those who have compared our mental world to a mirror are right.

"We reflect the images that surround us and we send others the images we create.

"And since we cannot escape the imperative of attraction,

we can only manifest clarity and beauty if we instill clarity and beauty in the mirror of our inner life.

"Depending on their nature, our mental reflections either favor our stagnation or they propel us on a journey forward, for each human individual lives in the heaven or hell that he or she has made for him or herself in the innermost recesses of the heart and mind, independently of the physical body. If we look at life in its glorious eternity, death only amounts to a transition between two types of the same experience in the 'indestructible now'.

"We can see that mediumship has existed everywhere in the history of humankind.

"Holy missions and destructive wars, noble deeds and evil obsessions begin in the reflections of the individual or collective mind, combined with the sublime or degrading forces of the thoughts that nurture them.

"Therefore, let us cultivate our education to perfect ourselves each and every day.

"We are all mediums in the lines of work in which we are situated.

"Psychic strength at this or that level of expression is peculiar to all, but there is no mediumistic improvement without purification of the individual.

"It is counterproductive to intensify the movement of energy without controlling its impulses.

"It is dangerous to possess something without knowing how to use it.

"The mirror buried in the mud cannot reflect the splendor of the sun.

"A riled lake cannot reflect the image of the star situated in the infinite.

"Let us raise our standard of knowledge through well-conducted study; let us purify the quality of our emotions by continuously exercising the higher virtues if we want to receive messages from great souls.

"Mediumship on its own is not enough.

"We have to know what type of mental wavelength we are assimilating in order to recognize the quality of our work and evaluate our direction."

Alberio continued with his invaluable comments and later responded to the hard questions asked by several students. On my part, I had collected extensive material to ponder, and for that reason, together with Hilario, I said goodbye to our instructors with a few words of gratitude. Aulus promised to meet with us again on the following day.

2
The Psychoscope

When we met Aulus the following evening, he welcomed us with the same graciousness as the day before.

"I believe I have charted out our plan," he told us paternally. He paused, observed us attentively, and continued.

"I think we should focus our observations on a small group where we find better quality at our disposal. We have a group of ten incarnate colleagues, four of whom possess developed mediumistic faculties and a respectable moral foundation. It is a small group that serves an organization dedicated to our Christianizing endeavor. From this base-group, it will be possible for us to expand our observations and gather valuable notes for our work."

He gazed at us kindly in silence for an instant and added:

"We will do it this way because you want to focus your study of mediumship only on the terrestrial sphere since the subject would be much less complex here in our sphere of activity."

"Yes," Hilario and I agreed. "We want to be of some kind of assistance to our incarnate brothers and sisters as they carry out their tasks. For that reason, this opportunity has come to us as a true blessing."

After a few minutes of a warm conversation, Aulus kindly invited us:

"So, let's go. There's no time to lose."

He picked up a small box, and perhaps noticing our curiosity, he patiently explained:

"This is a psychoscope. It will facilitate our examinations and studies without the need for intense mental concentration."

I picked up the enigmatic instrument as I accepted the pleasure of carrying it. I could tell that on earth the tiny object would have weighed no more than a few grams.

Pricked by curiosity as much as I was, Hilario immediately asked:

"A psychoscope? What kind of contraption is that?"

"It's an apparatus that an illustrious student of spirit phenomenology intuitively referred to at the end of the last century. It's designed to probe the soul. It has the power to define the soul's vibrations and the ability to make diverse observations regarding the subject," Aulus explained with a smile. "We hope that in the future it will be available to human beings. It runs on electricity and magnetism, utilizing radiant elements similar in essence to gamma rays. It is composed of lenses for observation that can also be used for microphotography."

As we were on our way to the city down on the earth where we were to work, our mentor explained further:

"In our supervisory efforts, we can easily classify the perspectives of this or that group of psychic services. By analyzing the psychoscopy of a person or team of workers, we can assess their potential and categorize their situation. According to the radiations they project, we can plot out the work they are capable of achieving over time."

My colleague and I couldn't hide our surprise.

Amid amazement and apprehensiveness, Hilario ventured to ask:

"Does that mean that any one of us can be submitted to such an examination?"

"Certainly," Aulus answered good-naturedly. "We are all subject to being probed by the higher planes, just as we currently investigate the planes situated below ours. If the spectroscope enables a person to investigate the nature of the chemical elements found at enormous distances by analyzing the light waves they emit, we can much more easily discern the qualities of a person by the rays he or she emits. Morality, sentiments, education and character are clearly discernible through a brief inspection."

"What if elements rooted in evil show up in a group of workers for the good?" asked Hilario. "If the Spirit Instructors had a printout from the psychoscope, could they have them expelled?"

"That wouldn't be necessary. If most of the group remains dedicated to practicing the good, the few prisoners of evil would eventually leave due to a lack of affinity."

"But what happens in an institution whose noble program degenerates into disharmony, causing us to realize that virtue there is nothing more than a fictitious banner hiding ignorance and perversity?"

"In that case," responded Aulus tolerantly, "we wouldn't resort to any form of intervention or denunciation. Life itself is in charge of placing each of us where we belong."

Smiling, he added:

"The Angels or Ministers of Eternal Wisdom safely deliver us to the renovating forges of time and trial. On earth, it's currently known that it takes sixteen centuries for one gram of radium to lose half its weight, and that a cyclotron, working with atomic projectiles accelerated to millions of electron volts, immediately transmutes chemical elements. The slow evolution over the course of millennia or the abrupt shock of suffering alters our mental panorama, improving its character."

These comments compelled us to digress to other areas.

The Assistant displayed a brilliant intellectual background, allied with an extreme ease at explaining things.

I was about to ask some questions not directly related to the subject, but guessing my intent, Aulus stated:

"All worthwhile conversation is instructive, but for now, let's keep to the spirit of the task at hand. Success doesn't make attention unnecessary. If we were to digress into chemistry, it would only delay us."

With our objectives readjusted, Hilario pointed out:

"The psychoscope itself is a motive for important considerations. Just think of a human society that could expose the inner life of its members! It would save an enormous amount of time in the solution of numerous psychological problems."

"Yes," added our mentor cordially, "the future holds wonders for ordinary people's senses."

We reached the gate to the spacious building that the Assistant said was the sanctuary we were to visit and serve.

"This is the Christian Spiritist center that will serve as the starting point for our experiences and observations."

We went in.

Crossing a large enclosure containing several unfortunate spirits from our plane, our guide explained:

"This is the hall dedicated to public teaching. However, the place we are headed for is situated in an inner area, somewhat like the location of the heart within the body."

A short time later, we entered a small room in which a small group was gathered in silent mental concentration.

"Our colleagues," explained the Assistant, "are doing the preparatory harmonization: fifteen minutes of prayer, a talk or a reading with high moral content. They know they shouldn't approach the spirit world without the noble and worthy attitude that will enable them to attract edifying company. That is why they never attend a meeting like this without bringing the seeds of their best qualities to the realm that is invisible to them."

Hilario and I were inclined to inquire further; however, the respectability of the premises imposed silence.

Fellow spirits from our sphere were praying, compelling us to profound contemplation.

The Assistant prepared the psychoscope and after a quick assessment, asked us to examine it.

When it was my turn, the peculiarities of the apparatus amazed me.

Without any mental effort, I noticed that all the expressions of physical matter took on a different appearance, especially the matter from our plane.

The roof, the walls and other commonplace objects revealed themselves to be formed of currents of energy emitting a hazy glow.

I turned around to contemplate the incarnates. They now appeared to be more closely associated with one another by means of broad radiant circles that hovered over their heads in opal-like splendor.

I had the impression of seeing a corona of solar light around the opaque block of semi-dark mass to which the table had been reduced. The corona was comprised of ten individual points. The center of each one of them projected the spiritual faces of the praying incarnates.

From that chain of golden focal points, a wide band of violet light extended outward. This band appeared to be contained within another band of orangey light overflowing in diverse tones, which I couldn't identify, because my attention was fixed on the circle of illuminated faces visibly united like ten tiny suns all connected to each other. I noticed that above each of them was a halo of nearly-vertical, shiny, moving beams of light that looked like small antennae of smoldering gold. These halos differed from one incarnate to the next, and abundant clusters of stellar luminosity fell on each one from On High. When they touched the heads of those gathered there, they seemed like soft currents of energy that turned into microscopic petals that flickered with light and then went out in myriads of delicate and whimsical forms, gravitating momentarily around the brains where they were produced, like short-lived satellites swirling around the vital founts from which they emanated.

Spirit mentors guarded the assembly, each one radiating his or her own light.

Because the brothers and sisters from the physical plane were so attuned to the illuminated wave in which they were gathered, I asked enthusiastically:

"Aulus, my friend, are these brothers and sisters by any chance high order initiates of the Divine Revelation?"

Our mentor made a good-humored gesture and replied:

"No. We are still very far from such apostles. This is a group of four sisters and six brothers of goodwill. They are just regular people. They eat, drink, get dressed and present themselves like everyone else in the routines of earthly living. However, their minds are set on the high ideals of active faith expressed in love for their fellow beings. They try to discipline themselves; they exercise self-denial, and they cultivate constant goodness. Through their personal efforts in goodness and well-conducted study, they have acquired a high level of mental radiation.

Hilario, who had used the psychoscope first, added in the admiring tone of a surprised child:

"But what about the light? The matter we are familiar with on the earth looks to be transfigured. Everything here has taken on a new clarity! The sight is magnificent!"

"There is nothing so strange about it," replied the Assistant kindly. "Don't you know that an incarnate individual is a generator of electromagnetic power, with one oscillation per second registered by the heart? Are you by chance unaware of the fact that all living substances on earth emit energies, framed in the bands of ultraviolet radiations? Our friends here are souls that have evolved normally under appreciable vibratory conditions because of their sincere devotion to the good and disregard for their personal desires. Thus, they can project mental rays of sublimation, assimilating higher currents and enriching the vital rays of which they are common dynamos."

"Vital rays?" asked my colleague, seeking clarification.

"Yes. For a clearer definition, let's call them 'ectoplasmic rays', to use the technical vocabulary of modern Spiritists. These rays are peculiar to all living beings. It is through them that the caterpillar carries out its complex demonstrations of metamorphosis, and it is also based on them that all mediumistic materializations occur, since the incarnate sensitives that produce them liberate such energies more readily. All individuals have them, however, and emit them at a frequency that varies with each individual, according to the tasks that their Life Plan has assigned to them."

And optimistically he added:

"The study of mediumship rests on the foundations of the mind with its prodigious field of radiations. Knowledge about these rays will soon start a great renewal in the intellectual sectors of the world. Let's wait for the future."

Immediately thereafter, Aulus invited us for a more direct inspection and we gladly accompanied him.

3
The Mediumistic Team

"Let's get acquainted with our mediumistic team," said Aulus.

Stopping beside the incarnate friend in charge of directing the meeting, he added:

"This is our brother Raul Silva. He directs this group with sincere devotion to fraternity. He is correct in the performance of his duties and ardent in his faith; thus, he balances the group with the comprehension and goodwill that is characteristic of him. Through the love with which he carries out his task, he is the faithful instrument of discarnate benefactors, who have found his mind to be a crystalline mirror that reproduces their instructions."

He then approached a very young woman and explained:

"This is our sister Eugenia, a medium of great willingness whose glowing future in the expansion of the good seems promising. She's an excellent instrument of transmission that effectively assists with helping disoriented discarnates. With a clear intuition combined with her moral standing, she has the advantage of remaining conscious during the communications, thereby benefiting our field of action."

Next, he stopped to the left of a young man approximately thirty years old, and said:

"This is our friend Anelio Araujo. He has been gradually progressing in clairvoyance, clairaudience and psychography."

Then, approaching a kindly gentleman, he stated:

"This is our Antonio Castro, a well-intentioned young man with great potential to take part in our activities. However, being a somnambulist, his passivity requires great watchfulness on our part. He leaves his physical body easily and performs valuable tasks with us; however, he still needs more study and broader experience to express himself more clearly about his personal observations. Sometimes, when out of his body, he behaves like a child, and that compromises our work. When he lends his body to demented or suffering discarnates so that they can communicate, he requires our special care. He tends to leave his body at the mercy of the communicating spirits, whereas it is his obligation to assist us in containing them, so that our fraternal efforts do not result in injury to his physical body. Nonetheless, he will be a valuable assistant in our studies."

Moving along a little more, the Assistant stopped in front of a respectable woman praying fervently, and explained:

"I would like to introduce our sister Celina, a devoted companion of our spiritual ministry. She has already passed through half a century of physical existence and has won significant victories in her moral battles. A widow for almost twenty years, she has dedicated herself to her children with admirable valor, overcoming thorny obstacles and dark days of self-denial. She was able to heroically withstand attacks by ignorant and unfortunate legions of spirits that surrounded her husband, whom she had married in order to fulfill a sacrificial task. She experienced the persecution of diabolical spirits but refused to surrender, and she struggled for many years to irreproachably fulfill the obligations which the world had assigned to her. She refined her mediumistic faculties in the flames of moral suffering, as you would refine pieces of iron through the action of fire and anvil. She is not a mere instrument of psychic phenomena – she's a selfless servant in the building of spiritual values. Clairvoyance, clairaudience, somnambulistic incorporation and out-of-body faculties are states she can enter with the same spontaneity with which she breathes, while staying attentive to her responsibilities; hence, she is a valuable co-worker in our endeavors. Diligent and humble, she has found her greatest joy in the sowing of fraternal love. Distributing her time between obligations and edifying study, she has transformed herself into a spiritual accumulator of beneficent energies, assimilating elevated mental currents that make her less accessible to the forces of darkness."

In fact, standing next to Dona[3] Celina, we enjoyed a wonderful sensation of peace and comfort.

Most likely enraptured by the wave of indefinable happiness that enveloped us, Hilario asked:

"If we were to make a psychoscopic examination of Dona Celina right now, would her condition, as we are registering it, be duly characterized?"

"Perfectly," responded Aulus immediately. "It would pick up her fluidic emanations of kindness and understanding, faith and courage. Just as scientific studies on earth catalogue the chemical elements that form dense matter, in our field of rarefied matter it is possible to analyze the type of subtle forces emitted by each being. Later on, human beings will be able to examine emissions of optimism or confidence, sadness or desperation and assess their density and limits, just as they can already separate

---

3   In Portuguese, a term of respect used with a woman's first name. – Tr.

and study radiations from uranium atoms. Mental principles are measurable and will merit exceptional attention in the future. That is happening right now with photons studied by scientists engaged in deciphering the specific composition of light."

After a brief pause the Assistant added:

"More than anything else, a psychoscopic examination appraises the nature of our thoughts, and through such an assessment, it is very easy to evaluate our merits as well as our needs."

Our guide invited us to participate in a detailed examination of sister Celina's encephalic area, pointing out:

"In every mediumistic process, we have to remember that the brain is the organ through which the mind manifests. You obviously already possess enough knowledge about that organic apparatus, so we don't need to focus our attention on the technical details of the physical body."

He caressed her head of graying hair and added:

"A succinct examination of her brain's life will suffice since it is there that the keys to the communication between the mental and physical worlds are kept."

Focusing our attention by means of a small lens that Aulus handed to us, Celina's brain looked like a powerful radio station with thousands of antennae and conductors, resistors and connections of microscopic proportions used by cells specialized in diverse services, functioning as detectors and stimulants, transformers and amplifiers of sensations and ideas, whose vibrations shone within as incessant rays illuminating a miniscule firmament.

The Assistant, too, observed that marvelous labyrinth in which the epiphysis[4] shone like a tiny blue sun, and said:

"We won't point out details related to the brain or the nervous system in general, since you are already familiar with them through your ordinary human knowledge."

---

[4] Pineal Gland – Tr.

At that instant, I was amazed to notice the beams of association between the cortical cells as they vibrated from the passage of the magnetic flow of thoughts.

"Let's remember," continued our instructor, "that the delicate encephalic apparatus is composed of millions of cells that perform individual functions like workers in a hierarchical order within a harmonious governmental structure."

And specifying certain regions of that prodigious thinking realm section by section, he stated:

"There's no need to extend our digressions. The experiences acquired by the soul constitute a marvelous synthesis of perception and sensibility in our condition as free spirits, but they are specified in the apparatus of dense matter as control centers for the manifestations of the individuality, fully open to analysis. This is how the incarnate soul possesses in the physical brain the special centers that govern the head, the face, the eyes, the ears and the limbs, together with the centers of speech, language, sight, hearing, memory, writing, taste, swallowing, touch, and smell; in addition, there are the centers for registering hot and cold, pain, and muscular equilibrium, as well as the inner qualities of the mind, the connection with the external world, the imagination, esthetic taste, the various artistic stimuli and all the many other acquisitions of experiences stored by the being. This being will win its own individuality, step by step and effort upon effort, ennobling it by constant work for full sublimation through all the opportunities of progress and perfection that earth can offer."

There was a brief, spontaneous pause.

And because Hilario and I didn't dare interrupt, the Assistant continued:

"We cannot perform any study of mediumistic faculties without a study of the personality. Thus, I regard it to be extremely important that we consider the brain centers that represent the bases of operation of thought and will, which understandably influence all mediumistic phenomena, from pure intuition to objective materialization. On many occasions, these resources – which merit the protection and aid of wise and benevolent spirits in their endeavors of love and sacrifice among human beings when their intermediaries uphold themselves in the superior ideals of kindness and service toward others – can be occupied by low order or animalized discarnate spirits in a lamentable process of obsession."

"But," Hilario interrupted judiciously, "with a brain as illuminated as that of our sister Celina, can we really believe that it may be invaded by less evolved intelligences? Is such a retrocession likely?"

"We mustn't forget," replied the Assistant, "that Celina is an incarnate soul involved in a long-term trial, and that in her duties as a learner she is far from finishing the lesson."

He thought for a moment and then philosophized good-humouredly:

"On a three hundred mile trip, many surprises can occur in the last mile."

Then placing his right hand on the medium's forehead, he continued:

"Our sister has borne her hardships with goodwill, a living faith, charity and patience. Just like us, she has not yet been able to fully free herself from her past debts. We are a vast legion of combatants seeking to overcome the enemies who inhabit our inner fortress or the world of our own selves. These enemies, symbolized by our past habits of living according to our lower nature, place us in attunement with the inhabitants of the darkness, and that is obviously perilous to our equilibrium.

"If our friend Celina, like any of us, were to abandon the discipline that we must adopt to keep our good reception of the light; if she were to yield to the calls of vanity or discouragement, which we usually imagine as being acquired rights or unjustifiable disenchantment, she would certainly experience a siege by destructive elements that would interrupt her currently noble evolutionary experience. Many mediums suffer losses of this type. After promising rehearsals and a brilliant start, they think they own spiritual resources that do not belong to them; or they fear the prolonged afflictions of the journey and retreat into uselessness, descending in their level of morality or yielding to unproductive inertia. They inevitably return to their primitive impulses, which incessant work in the good would have induced them to forget."

Then smiling, he added:

"We have not yet achieved the supreme victory over ourselves. We are in the condition of the earthly soil, which cannot produce without the help of the plough or the hoe. Without the tools of labor and struggle to perfect our abilities, we would be continuously threatened by hazardous weeds, which multiply and consolidate in direct relation to the aptitude of the abandoned soil.

Then, looking straight at us as if to emphasize the weight of the responsibilities with which we were vested, he concluded:

"Our spiritual achievements of the present are small glimmering beams of clarity over the dark pyramids of our past. A lot of caution is needed with the seeds of the good so that they are not swept away by the winds of evil. Thus, examined as a tool for the work of higher intelligences, the mediumistic endeavor is not that easy to be led righteously. Against the still-fragile channel that offers itself for the passage of the light, there are the heavy waves of the darkness of ignorance stirring densely around us."

The Assistant became quiet.

It seemed that he, too, was now connecting to the magnetic field of the group in silence, ready for the work of the meeting that was about to begin.

4
At Work

A gentle knock on the door caused one of the members of the group to leave the meditation circle and answer it.

Two patients – a young woman and an elderly gentleman – brought by two family members entered and sat in a corner of the room, outside the group's magnetic circle.

"Those are the patients who are to receive assistance," stated Aulus.

Soon thereafter, a coworker from our plane admitted several suffering and disturbed spirits who then stood before the assembly, forming a large group.

None of them were ill-at-ease in approaching us.

Instead, they gathered around the praying incarnates, like moths instinctively drawn to a bright light.

They had arrived noisily, uttering disconnected words or unedifying expressions. However, as soon as they came in contact with the spiritual emanations of the group, they fell silent, as if restrained by forces they could not perceive.

Aulus attentively informed us:

"These are disturbed souls who accompany incarnate relatives, friends or enemies to the center's public meetings. But they disconnect from them as soon as the incarnates let themselves be renewed by the salvific ideas expressed by those who provide the doctrinal teachings. Once the minds of those whom they habitually vampirize are changed, they feel like they have been evicted from their home, because as the train of thought of those to whom they attach themselves is changed, they experience sudden turns in the positions they are wrongly holding. Some rebel and flee from places of prayer such as this one, temporarily hating its assistance and arming new persecutions for their victims, whom they go looking for until they find them again. Others, however, are somewhat touched by the lessons they hear and remain on the premises in eager expectation, hungry for further enlightenment."

Hilario received this information with surprise and asked curiously:

"What happens when the incarnates pay no attention to the lessons?"

"They attend sanctuaries of faith like sealed vessels. Impervious to good suggestions, they continue to be inaccessible to the change they need so much."

"Is this same phenomenon repeated in temples of other religious faiths?"

"Yes. The spoken word plays a significant role in the building of the spirit. As long as they are inspired by the Infinite Good, sermons and lectures by clergy and religious instructors of different faiths have moral growth as their objective."

The Assistant thought for a moment and added:

"However, while it's hard for people to cultivate a worthy life, it's even harder for them to get ready for a liberating death. The soul usually discarnates without having rid itself of thoughts that are entangled in situations, persons and earthly matters. Consequently, the mind continues to be imprisoned by the nearly-always inferior interests of the world; it remains crystallized and sickly within disquieting scenes it has created for itself. Hence the value of proper religious worship because it creates an environment suitable for spiritual growth and has indispensable advantages not only for incarnates who sincerely and fervently participate in it, but also for discarnates who aspire to their own transformation. During public worship, all sanctuaries are filled with needy souls who attend without their dense bodies, thirsting for relief. Proclaimers of the good word can be compared to electricians, disconnecting mental 'plugs' through the liberating principles they spread in the sphere of thought."

He smiled amiably and continued:

"That is why vampirizing spirits work against such speakers, quite often enveloping their listeners in soporific fluids that make them sleepy in order to delay their renewal."

As I observed the troubled spirits gathered by the table in a semi-circle, I thought about using the psychoscope to examine them more closely. Aulus, however, immediately told me:

"That won't be necessary. A careful analysis will suffice to provide us with interesting results since our friends display their sufferings on their perispiritual bodies."

I noticed that Assistant Aulus did not want to prolong the conversation, probably because he was preparing to take part in the forthcoming work. Thus, I took advantage of those brief moments to observe the unfortunate discarnates bound closely together amid anguish and expectancy.

They appeared to be enveloped in a large oval cloud, like a thick, moving, dark gray fog agitated by strange formations.

I observed the whole group and noticed that some displayed infirmities, as if they were still in the flesh.

Wounded limbs, deformities, paralyses and various ulcerations were perceptible at a quick glance.

Perhaps because Hilario and I were examining them closely, like students in a classroom, one of the meeting's spirit participants approached us and cordially explained:

"These suffering brothers and sisters all bear the stigma of the wrongs they deliberately committed. Infirmities that are the result of moral imbalance survive in the perispirit, nourished by the thoughts that originated them when such thoughts persist after the death of the corporeal body."

"But do they show improvement at mediumistic meetings?" asked Hilario, astonished.

"Yes," he responded. "They assimilate new ideas and start to use them, albeit slowly, thereby improving their inner vision and structuring new destinies. Mental renewal is the renewal of life."

I thought about the illusion of those who see death as being the soul's free ticket to heaven or hell as final places of happiness or sorrow ...

How few are those who are aware that we bring with us the marks of our thoughts, activities and accomplishments, and that the grave is nothing more than the photographic developer bath for the images we hid in the world under the garment of flesh!

Consciousness is a center of forces, around which the good and the evil generated by consciousness itself gravitate; and right there, we had come face to face with a vast rank of souls suffering in the different purgatories characteristic of them.

We approached a sad discarnate who wore an emaciated expression and Hilario, on a purely human impulse, asked him:

"Friend, what is your name?"

"My name?" he stammered.

After a huge but futile effort to remember, he answered:

"I don't have a name."

"Impossible," replied an astonished Hilario. "We all have names."

"I've forgotten... I've forgotten everything," responded the wretch despondently.

"This is a case of amnesia that needs to be studied," clarified a member from the work team we were visiting.

"Is this a natural phenomenon?" asked Hilario, perplexed.

"Yes, it may be natural due to some kind of imbalance brought from earth, but it's possible that our friend is being victimized by a powerful post-hypnotic suggestion that may have originated with a persecutor that had great power over his mnemonic resources. Our friend is still profoundly attached to physical sensations, and his mental life is still a copy of the sensorial forms he left behind. Seen from this point of view, he is probably under the control of foreign and contemptible wills with which he may have been associated while on earth."

"Good God!" responded Hilario, quite impressed. "Is such control after death possible?"

"And why not? Death is merely the continuation of life, and in life – which is eternal – we get what we ask for."

Attentive to our studies on mediumship, I remarked:

"If our amnesiac friend were taken to a medium, would he communicate like this, not knowing his own identity?"

"Absolutely. He would require a caring treatment like any ordinary mental case. Speaking through any medium that might grant him access, he would display for any earthly counselor the same enigma that we are now witnessing."

At that moment, a spirit in a deplorable state came near us.

He was a thin, sad man and his right arm was paralyzed and withered.

Responding to my questioning glance and appearing to have little time to spare in fraternal conversation, our colleague only said,

"Examine him and draw your own conclusions."

I gently touched his forehead and sensed his anguish.

In the crystallized memories of his mental world, I perceived his inner drama.

He had been a well-muscled stevedore on the docks, a die-hard drunkard who returned home one day and slapped his father's face because the old man disapproved of his conduct.

Unable to return the attack, the old man, spitting blood, shouted mercilessly:

"You bastard! May your cruel arm turn into a dry stick ... May you be damned!"

Upon hearing those words, which were accompanied by a terrifying stream of hypnotic power, the son went back out on the street. Distraught by the curse hurled at him, he got drunk in order to forget.

As he staggered around, he got hit by a street-car and lost his arm.

He lived for a few more years but during that time, he crystallized in his mind the idea that his father's words had had the power of a vengeful command and had become implanted in the depths of his soul. Thus, upon discarnating, his perispiritual body recovered his formerly severed limb, but due to his fixed idea, it hung, withered and inert.

As I was reflecting on all this, our mentor approached, and perceiving what was happening, he informed us:

"This is a very difficult case of readjustment, requiring time and tolerance."

And placing his hands on the shoulders of the paralytic, he added:

"Our friend's mind is subjugated by remorse. He harbors within himself the curse he received. He will require a lot of loving care to recover."

Without digressing from the subject, I inquired:

"If he were to utilize a medium to communicate, would he transmit to the human receptor the sensations he now harbors?"

"Yes," confirmed the Assistant. "He would reflect in the passive medium the impressions that have taken him over, according to the magnetizing processes in which the services of interchange are based."

He smiled kindly and added:

"However, let's not lose our focus in individual cases for now. Each of the imbalanced spirits here has brought his or her own disquieting experiences. Let's observe this from a higher viewpoint."

He then led me to the head of the table, where our friend Raul Silva was about to say a prayer.

5
The Assimilation of Mental Currents

Just two minutes before 8 p.m., the spirit director responsible for the meeting entered the small room.

Our guide introduced everyone.

Brother Clementino greeted us warmly.

"This place belongs to all of us," he said with a smile, inviting us to feel at ease in carrying out the task entrusted to us.

At that moment, various spirits from our plane approached the mediums who would participate in that evening's work.

Clementino moved to Raul Silva's side, where he stood in silent reflection.

Soon thereafter, Aulus invited me to look through the psychoscope. Adjusting it to a different modality, he recommended a careful examination.

I focused on the mediums immersed in mental concentration and saw them in a different aspect.

This time, their physical bodies were like high tension electromagnetic currents.

The nervous system, the glands and the various plexuses emitted a particular luminescence. Juxtaposed on the brain, the mind appeared as a sphere of distinctive light, each person with his or her particular radiation potential.

Acknowledging our curiosity, the Assistant explained:

"In any mediumistic study, we mustn't forget that, while in the flesh, the spiritual individuality resides in the atomic citadel of the physical body, formed by resources taken on loan from the earth's environment. Blood, brain, nerves, bones, skin and muscles represent elements agglutinated for the temporary manifestation of the soul on the earth, constituting its temporary garment according to the conditions of the mind."

At that instant, brother Clementino placed his hand on Raul's forehead, while his figure, from our standpoint, became more human-like – almost opaque.

"Our spirit benefactor and director," explained Aulus, "appears denser because he has lowered his normally elevated vibration to match Raul's vibratory level as far as possible in order to begin the task at hand. He is now acting upon Raul's brain, somewhat like an emeritus musician would respectfully handle a highly valuable violin. whose firmness and harmony he recognizes."

We noticed that Clementino's venerable head had begun to emit flashes of light. At the same time, Raul's brain, under the influence of the benefactor's hand, acquired an intense luminosity, albeit of a different kind.

The discarnate mentor lifted up his moving voice, asking for the Divine Blessing with words familiar to us. Raul transmitted them in a loud voice with very little variation.

As emotion took hold of our hearts, a gentle silence ensued for a few quick minutes.

Threads of shining light connected the participants at the table, and we saw that the prayer had brought them together more completely.

The prayer over, I approached Raul.

I wanted to investigate more deeply the sensations that had come over his physical body. I noticed that his upper torso, including his arms and hands, were enveloped by a vigorous wave of energy that caused goose bumps on his skin – a phenomenon of gentle exaltation similar to a "pleasant shiver." This wave of energy came to rest on his solar plexus, where it became a luminous stimulus that spread through the nervous system to the brain, and then flowed from his mouth in the form of words.

Following my analysis, the Assistant explained:

"Brother Clementino's stream of mental forces has acted upon Raul's psychic organization like a current sent to an electric bulb. From the solar plexus, it rose toward the neuro-cerebral system, similar to the electricity from a power plant which, at reaching the bulb, spreads through the incandescent filament to produce light."

"And what about the 'voltage' problem?" I inquired curiously.

"It hasn't been overlooked. Clementino has gradated his thoughts and expressions according to Raul's capacity, as well as that of the surrounding environment, adjusting himself according to what they can handle, much like when the electrician controls the flow of energy according to the network of receiver elements."

He smiled and added:

"Each recipient receives according to his or her own capacity."

Aulus's comparisons suggested interesting questions. The electrical connection generates the light in a bulb. But what about in this case? From what we could tell, the spiritual contact obviously generated energies flowing from Raul's brain and mouth in the form of luminous rays and words.

The instructor perceived our mute inquiry and hastened to explain:

"The bulb, within which the light is produced, emits photons, which are the living elements of nature vibrating in 'physical space' through movements particular to them. Likewise, our soul, within which the radiating idea is processed, emits the spiritual elements, condensed in the multiple and ponderable energy of thought. In turn, we influence the 'mental space' with these elements. Worlds act on one another through the radiating energies they emit, and souls influence one another through the mental agents they produce."

Our mentor's precise and serene words compelled us to reflect, albeit briefly.

His clear explanations regarding mental energy led me to an invaluable conclusion: thought cannot escape the realities of the corpuscular world.

Just as we on earth have an understanding of the chemistry of dense matter by cataloguing its atomic units, the mental field offers broad opportunities for studying its combinations ... Thoughts of cruelty, rebelliousness, sadness, love, comprehension, hope and joy would thus possess differentiated natures with their own characteristics and weights, rendering the soul more dense or subtle, besides defining its magnetic qualities as well ... The mental wave would thus possess specific coefficients of energy, whether in silent concentration, speech or written words.

In this way, I understood once more and without hindrance that we are naturally victims or beneficiaries of our own creations according to the mental currents we project. We thereby enslave ourselves to the liabilities of our past or liberate ourselves for the forefront of progress according to our decisions and activities, in harmony or disharmony with the Eternal Laws.

This soliloquy didn't last long.

Our mentor, attentive to the objectives of our presence at the center, asked:

"Did you notice the communion between Clementino and Raul during the prayer?"

Seeing our expectation as learners, he continued:

"We have just seen the phenomenon of the perfect assimilation of mental currents that usually preside over nearly all mediumistic phenomena. To clarify, let's compare Raul, our incarnate coworker, to a receiving apparatus like those used in broadcasting. By condensing his thought and will, Clementino's mental emissions envelope Raul in a profusion of rays that reach his inner field, first through the pores of the skin, which are myriads of antennae upon which the emissions take on the aspect of weak and indistinct impressions. These impressions connect with the spirit body's centers, which act like condensers, and immediately reach the cables of the nervous system, which in turn perform the role of induction coils. There, impressions accumulate in an instant and then are automatically reconstituted in the brain, where we possess hundreds of motor centers, similar to a miraculous keyboard of electromagnets linked to each other, and in whose dynamic center mental actions and reactions are processed, determining creative vibrations through thought or speech, with the brain acting as a powerful broadcasting and receiving station and the mouth as a loudspeaker. Such stimuli are also expressed through the mechanisms of the hands and feet, or through the senses and organs, which operate in the manner of cranes and conductors, transformers and analyzers under the direct command of the mind."

His explanation could not have been simpler; however, it still offered an opportunity for broader questions.

"So, is this the technique of thought itself?" asked Hilario with great interest.

"Not exactly," answered the mentor. "Thought, which is exclusive to each of us, flows incessantly from our brain like the heat and magnetic waves that are unique to each of us, and we normally use it to activate the resources we have."

"But it's not so easy to tell the difference between our own mental creation and one that comes into our head from others," pondered my intrigued colleague.

"Your assertion is groundless," replied the Assistant. "Any person who knows how to manage his or her attention can tell the difference since our thoughts vibrate at a unique frequency that comes across in our specific mode of expression, habits and points of view and in the manner and style that are particular to us."

He then added amiably:

"In matters of this type, we must be very careful in our judgments. While we align our criterion with earthly standards, our mental life is almost always parasitic since we hide our thought waves in order to reflect and act within established prejudices or the pragmatism of pre-established customs – which are mental crystallizations in time – or we follow the fashion of the day and the opinions of our friends, all constituting an easy accommodation that requires less effort. But it would be enough to practice meditation, to study constructively and to get into the habit of discerning in order to understand where our line of thought lies, thus clearly identifying the spiritual currents that we are assimilating."

Hilario thought for a few moments, and showing on his face the satisfaction of someone who has made an important discovery, he said quite pleased:

"Now I can see how mediumistic phenomena can occur in the simple situations of life, as well as in notable deeds of excellence and in daily dramas."

"Yes, yes," our mentor agreed, now concerned about the amount of time our conversation was taking. "Mediumship is a gift inherent to all individuals, just like the faculty of breathing, and each person assimilates the higher or lower energies with which he or she is in tune. That is why the Divine Master recommends prayer and vigilance so that we do not fall prey to the suggestions of evil. Temptation is a thread of living forces radiating from us, capturing elements that are similar to it, and thus weaving around our soul a thick web of impulses that sometimes become irresistible."

And then, taking his place in the ongoing meeting, he added:

"Let's study as we work. The time utilized in serving others is a blessing that we accumulate on our behalf forever."

6
Conscious Psychophony[5]

The mediumistic meeting at the Spiritist Center was proceeding harmoniously.

Three spirit guards entered the room, escorting an unfortunate brother who was to receive the group's assistance.

He was an unhappy, discarnate bachelor, who had no idea of his present situation.

Incapable of seeing his escorts, he walked like a deaf and blind person, impelled by powers that he couldn't identify.

"This is an unfortunate obsessor whom they have just removed from the environment where he had been staying for a long time," said Aulus compassionately. "He discarnated in his prime after wearing himself out on wild partying. Lethal toxification destroyed his body at a time when he did not have the least bit of preparation to understand the truths of the spirit."

And like someone who had been informed beforehand regarding the particularities of the case, Aulus continued:

---

[5] Psychophony: communications by speaking mediums. – Tr.

"Observe. This is someone living in his own darkness. He has been brought to this room unaware of the route taken by his own feet, like any serious mental patient. After he left his garment of flesh with his thoughts fixed on his passion for a woman – presently a tormented, very sick person who had tuned in to him to the point of keeping him at her side amidst tears and afflictions – he began to vampirize her physical body. The loss of his physical vessel while spiritually deficient left him completely disoriented like a shipwrecked person in the middle of the night. However, he adapted himself to the physical body of the beloved woman, whom he began to obsess. He found her to be a new instrument of sensation by seeing through her eyes, hearing through her ears, often speaking through her mouth, and vitalizing himself with the ordinary food she ingests. They have lived for almost five years in this symbiosis, but the disturbed and undernourished woman has begun to display significant organic imbalances. Because she has requested our assistance, we have to perform a double rescue. In order for her to be cured of the phobias that presently assault her as reflections from his mind, which is terrified before the realities of the spirit, we have to remove the fluids that surround her, just as a tree strangled by the embrace of the vine has to have them cleared away so that it can recover."

Meanwhile, the spirit guards obeyed Clementino's orders and placed the sufferer next to Eugenia.

The center's mentor approached her and applied magnetic energies over her cerebral cortex after projecting luminous rays over an extensive area of the glottis.

We watched as Eugenia-spirit left her body, although she remained close to it at a distance of a few inches. Aided by the helpers, the visitor sat very close to Dona Eugenia, leaning over her, assuming the posture of someone bending over a windowsill.

As I watched the scene, I recalled the way things work in the vegetable kingdom, wherein one plant develops at the cost of another, and I understood that that association could be compared to the subtle process of neuro-psychic grafting.

Sighs of relief came from the medium's chest; for a while, she had been somewhat agitated.

I noticed that light shiny threads linked Eugenia's forehead – she was now disengaged from her body – to the communicating spirit's brain.

Because I gave Aulus a questioning look, he explained solicitously:

"This is conscious psychophony, that is, the work of a speaking medium. Although he has appropriated Eugenia's energies, the sickly guest from our plane remains under her control, connected to her magnetically through the nervous system, through which our sister will be informed of all the words he mentalizes and intends to say. In fact, he has temporarily taken possession of our sister's vocal cords and has appropriated her sensorial world; hence, he can see, hear and reason with a certain amount of equilibrium by using her energies. Eugenia, in turn, has firm control over the reigns of her own will, acting as if she were a nurse playing along with the whims of a patient in order to help him. This whim, however, must be limited, because, aware of all the intentions of the unfortunate discarnate to whom she has lent her physical body, she reserves the right to correct any undesirable conduct he might display. Through the nervous system current, she will know his words as he forms them, discerning them beforehand because his mental impulses are reverberating in her thoughts like hammer blows. Thus, she can stop any abuse by monitoring his objectives and expressions, something she can do because he is a spirit who is morally beneath her in his present state of disturbance and suffering. Eugenia must not stoop to his level if she wants to be of any use to him. Every spirit in disturbance is mentally infirm and requires assistance. In charitable sessions such as this, the first assistant is the medium, but if the medium falls into the vibratory pattern of the one seeking his or her help, there is little hope for an effective assistance. Thus, when mediums are aware of their responsibilities, they have the duty to cooperate in preserving order and respectability in the task of assisting discarnates, allowing them free manifestation only to the point where the manifestation does not collide with the harmony required for the group and with the dignity of the premises."

"So," added Hilario, "in this work, the medium is never very far away from his or her own body."

"That's right. Whenever the task involves disturbed spirits, the intermediary should not be too far away ... With a deranged person in our home, being away from it is dangerous; but if it is looked after by conscientious friends, we can take a long trip because it will be safely guarded. In rendering assistance to disturbed spirits, our presence is logically imperative."

He gazed at Eugenia, who remained alert and vigilant next to the spirit patient about to speak, and pointed out:

"If need be, our friend can return to her body instantly. They are both momentarily joined in a union in which the communicator represents the action, but the medium personifies the will. In all fields of work, it is natural for the superior to be responsible for the inferior."

The visitor put his hand over his face in a gesture of relief and exclaimed in astonishment:

"I can see! I can see! But what sort of spell is tying me down? What chains hold me to this heavy object?"

And accenting his expression of surprise, he continued:

What is the purpose of this gloomy, silent assembly? Who brought me here? Who brought me here?!"

We saw that, although outside her physical body, Eugenia heard all the words flowing from her mouth, temporarily being used by the pilgrim from the darkness, automatically storing them in her memory center.

"Upon making contact with the energy from the medium's nervous system," explained the Assistant, "the sufferer's senses have become revived, and that dazzles him. He is complaining about the chains that bind him, chains that are fifty percent the result of Eugenia's cautious containment. In this way, he behaves like a patient under control, which in this case is indispensable."

"What if our sister were to relax her authority?" Hilario asked curiously.

"She wouldn't be in a condition to lend him any concrete benefit, because then she would have descended to the derangement of the 'beggar for light', whom we propose to help."

With a happy image to illustrate the matter, Aulus added:

"A passive medium in such circumstances may be compared to a surgical operating table holding the patient in need of medical assistance. If there is a lack of firmness and humility, any intervention would be totally impossible."

"But does our friend consciously see the spirit now associated to her physical body as clearly as we do?" I asked, attentive to my learning objectives.

"In Eugenia's case, that does not occur, because her efforts to protect her own energies, along with her interest in assisting to the best of her abilities, do not allow her the necessary mental concentration to see his outer form. However, his afflictions and pains are reproduced in her. She feels his pain and distress, registering both his suffering and his discomfort."

While our conversation was broadening, the communicating spirit shouted:

"Is this some sort of court? Why this strange reception when I'm the one who's being inconvenienced by being here? I am Liborio dos Santos, and no one offends me without paying for it."

And as if his conscience were torturing him through inner creations not given to us to perceive, he yelled frantically:

"Who's accusing me of having despoiled my mother and then leaving her? I'm not responsible for the hardships of others... Aren't I worse off than her?"

Hilario looked compassionately at the obsessor and asked respectfully:

"Could his suffering be plain old mental anguish?"

"Not quite," clarified Aulus. "Mental crises of any degree affect us even in the vehicle of manifestation. The perispiritual brain of our brother is dilacerated and the affliction that has invaded his fluidic body is as real as that of an incarnate person suffering from an intracranial tumor."

Displaying great interest in the study, Hilario pointed out:

"Based on our desire for a greater understanding of spirit life, if we were incarnates at this meeting, could we submit him to a detailed questioning? Would he be able to identify himself fully well?"

Aulus shook his head slightly and said:

"In his present condition, such an undertaking wouldn't be viable. We are focusing only on an act of charity, but nonetheless, one of the highest significance for life itself. If we tried to question him, it would be fruitless. We would be addressing an alienated mind, which for some time to come will show damage in the critical centers of reasoning. He bears the legacy of an unbalanced existence and is strongly attracted to the woman who loves him and whose relentless persecutor he has become. For the time being, he aspires to nothing but a parasitic life with her, nourishing himself on her energies. He has enfolded her in sickly spiritual fluids and leans on her in the way a climbing vine spreads itself and proliferates on a fence ... Adding to this the shock produced by death, we don't have the right to expect him to give us a satisfactory and complete personal identification."

Meanwhile, the deranged Liborio continued:

"Who could stand a situation like this? Is someone hypnotizing me? Who's checking out my thoughts? What good is it to restore my sight if you tie down my arms?"

Observing him with fraternal sympathy, the Assistant informed us:

"He's complaining about the control he is being submitted to by Eugenia's cautious will."

Thinking about the questions that were burning in our souls, Hilario pondered:

"With the medium being conscious while she listens to the words of the spirit as he uses her vocal cords, it is possible that she might have some real doubts ... Mightn't she be led to believe that the words she is saying are her own? Could she have some hesitations?"

"That's possible. However, our sister can in fact tell that the turmoil and the words spoken at this time are not her own."

"But ... what if she did have doubts?" continued my colleague.

"Then, she would emit from her own mind an explicit refusal, expelling the communicating spirit and putting an end to a precious opportunity for service. Doubt, in this case, would be a halting wave of negative forces."

However, because Raul Silva had initiated the conversation with this rebellious guest, our guide invited us to observe the situation more closely.

7

Spiritual Rescue

Clementino's influence completely enveloped Raul, who stood up and spoke kindly to Liborio:

"My friend, let's stay calm and ask for divine help!"

"I'm sick, desperate..."

"Yes, none of us are well, but we mustn't lose faith. We are children of our Heavenly Father, who is always generous with His love."

"Are you a priest?"

"No, I'm just a brother."

"That's a lie; I don't even know you."

"We are all one family under God."

The troubled spirit laughed ironically and said:

"You must be some fanatical priest to talk like that."

Raul Silva's patience touched us. He didn't address Liborio as if he were an inhabitant of the darkness who was capable of awakening any impulse of tactless curiosity in him.

Notwithstanding the invaluable aid of the mentor who accompanied him, Raul himself expressed compassion mixed with unequivocal fatherly interest. He welcomed the guest without amazement or anger, but as if he were a disturbed family member who had come home.

Perhaps for this reason the obsessor in his turn became less angry. As soon as the patient began to dialogue somewhat better with the center's director, we noticed that Eugenia doubled her efforts in providing assistance.

"I'm not a religious minister," continued Raul calmly, "but I would like you to accept me as your friend."

"That's a laugh! Friends don't exist in times of misery ... Every friend I ever knew abandoned me. The only one left is Sara. I'll never leave her…"

With his gaze showing that his thought was fixed on the person he was referring to, he added with repressed indignation:

"I don't know why my movements are being restrained. That's pointless. I don't even know why I'm restraining myself. Any person who has been provoked to the extent that I have ought to come to blows with all of you ... Tell me, what are these silent men and women doing here? What do they want from me?"

"They are praying for your peace," said Raul in a kind and endearing tone of voice.

"So what! What do we have in common? Do I owe you anything?"

"Quite the contrary! We are the ones who owe you our attention and assistance. This is an institution of fraternal assistance; and it is beyond a doubt that, in a hospital, no one can rightly question the private struggle of those who knock at the door, because, more than anything else, it is the obligation of medicine and nursing to treat bleeding wounds."

Faced with this argument uttered with sincerity and simplicity, the obstinate, suffering Liborio seemed to become even calmer. Emissions of mental energy from Raul reached his chest area, as if looking for his heart.

Liborio tried to speak, but like a traveler who could no longer withstand the dryness of the desert, he was moved by the tenderness of that unexpected welcome rising before him like a fountain of cool water. Surprised, he found that the words stuck in his throat.

Under Clementino's wise command, the counselor spoke with great tenderness.

"Liborio, my brother!"

Those three words were spoken with such an inflection of fraternal benevolence that the guest could not contain the tears that sprang from the depths of his soul.

Raul came closer. With a luminous magnetic energy pouring from his hands, he laid them on Liborio and invited him:

"Let's pray!"

After a minute of silence and under Clementino's inspiration, Raul prayed lovingly.

"Divine Master, cast your compassionate gaze on our family united here...

Travelers of many pilgrimages, at this time we rest under the blessed tree of prayer and implore your help!

We are all indebted to you and we are all in pledge to your infinite kindness, like servants indebted to their master.

Although we pray for us all, we pray especially for this friend, whom you have surely sent to our hearts as if he were a sheep rejoining the fold or a flesh-and-blood brother returning home.

Master, grant us the joy of receiving him with open arms.

Seal our lips so that we may not inquire about his origin, but open our souls to the opportunity of having him with us in peace.

Lend inspiration to our words so that imprudence may not find its way to our tongue, deepening our brother's inner wounds. Help us maintain the respect we owe him.

Lord, we are certain that chance does not preside over your designs.

Your love, which invariably reserves the best for us each and every day, brings us closer to one another for righteous work.

Our souls are threads of life in your hands!

Adjust them so that we may obtain from On High the blessing of serving with you!

Our Liborio is one more brother who has come from afar, from remote horizons of the past...

Oh Lord, help us so that he may not find us proclaiming your name in vain!"

The visitor was weeping.

We could clearly see, however, that it was not the power of the words that were affecting him, but the radiant sentiment that structured them.

Raul Silva, under Clementino's radiating right hand, seemed enveloped in intense light.

"Dear God, what's happening to me?!" Liborio managed to cry out in tears.

Brother Clementino signaled to one of the workers from our plane. He quickly obliged, producing an interesting item that looked like a screen of very thin gauze with special devices and measuring approximately one yard square.

The meeting's spirit mentor turned a small key in one of the corners of the apparatus and the soft fabric became covered with a light, whitish, shimmering fluidic mass.

He then positioned himself next to Raul, who under his control, said to the communicant:

"Remember, my friend, remember! Appeal to your memory! Watch the pictures that unfold before your eyes."

Immediately, as if his attention were compulsively drawn to the screen, our guest focused on it. We watched in amazement as the sensitized rectangle displayed various scenes in which Liborio himself was the principal protagonist. Receiving them mentally, Raul began to describe them:

"Look, my friend! It's nighttime. The racket of voices can be heard in the distance… Your elderly mother is calling you to her bedside, asking for your help … She's exhausted … You're the only child she has left … Her last hope in a tormented life … Her sole support … The poor woman can tell that she is dying. Her difficulty in breathing is torturing her … Her heart problem is foretelling the end of her body … She's afraid. She says that she's afraid of being alone because it is Saturday during Carnival[6] and the neighbors have departed for the festivity. She looks like a frightened child … She gazes at you anxiously and begs you to stay … You respond that you are going out for only a few minutes, just long enough to get her medication … Then you immediately go to a drawer in an adjacent room and take the only money she has left: a few hundred *cruzeiros*[7], which you think will enable you to enjoy that illusory happiness at the nightclub … Spirit friends staying in your home approach you, imploring your help on behalf of the patient so close to death, but you show yourself impervious to any thought of compassion … You say a few hurried words to your sick mother and leave. Out on the street, you are joined by undesirable discarnate companions with whom you have an affinity … disturbed spirits, hypnotized by vice, with whom you are dragged into reckless pleasure … For three days and four nights, you surrender to madness, completely forgetful of all your obligations … Only at dawn on Wednesday do you

---

6 In Brazil, Carnival entails nearly a week of festivities, culminating on Tuesday, the day before Lent – Tr.

7 Brazilian currency at the time this book was written. – Tr.

return, semiconscious and drained ... The old woman, rescued by anonymous hands, no longer recognizes you ... She awaits her death with resignation, while you walk to a room in the back intending to refresh yourself with a bath ... You turn on the gas and sit down for a few minutes, your head spinning ... Your body is demanding sleep after such crazed revelry ... Irrepressible fatigue overcomes you ...You lose sense of yourself and you fall asleep, half drunk, losing your life to the toxic gases ... On a sunny morning, a funeral car delivers you to the morgue as a simple suicide."

At this point, the patient, as if waking from a nightmare, shouted desperately:

"Oh, that's the truth! The truth! ... Where's my home? Sara, Sara! I want my mother, my mother!"

"Calm down!" counseled Raul, compassionately. "We are never without divine assistance! Your home, my friend, closed its doors along with your eyes of flesh, and your mother is now in other spheres, extending her loving and sanctifying arms to you."

Overwhelmed, the communicating spirit fell into tears.

So great was his emotional crisis that the group's spirit mentor rushed to disconnect him from the mediumistic instrument, entrusting him to the spirit guards so that he could be appropriately sheltered in a nearby organization.

In a profound process of transformation, Liborio departed, and Eugenia resumed her normal position.

Because the screen had returned to its original transparency, I addressed our guide with some spontaneous questions.

"What was the function of that unfamiliar rectangle? What scenes were those that had so quickly appeared right before our very eyes?"

"That apparatus," Aulus kindly stated, "is an 'ectoplasm condenser'. It has the ability to concentrate the energy rays projected by the meeting's participants, thereby reproducing the images that flow from the communicating spirit's thoughts, not only for our own observation but also for analysis by the counselor, who receives them in his intuitive field, now aided by the magnetic energies from our plane."

"Obviously, the workings of such a mechanism must be extraordinary!" said Hilario, greatly impressed.

"It's nothing to marvel at, really. The spirit guest only gazes at the reflections of his own mind, much like a person who examines him or herself in a mirror."

"But if it is actually an energy condenser," I considered, "then we would have to conclude that the success of the endeavor would depend on the collaboration of all the members of the group."

"Precisely!" confirmed the Assistant. "The ectoplasmic energies are supplied by the group of incarnates for the benefit of those brothers and sisters who are still semi-materialized in the vibratory fields of the physical experience. That is why Raul Silva and Clementino require the concourse of the whole group so that the mechanism can function as harmoniously as possible. Individuals who exteriorize dishonorable sentiments, equivalent to poisonous principles arising from various types of degrading behavior, greatly interfere with activities of this nature, for they cast into the condenser the darkness they harbor, harming the effectiveness of the assembly and impeding the clear image on the screen for the spirit in need of comprehension and light."

The issue invited a great number of questions, but our guide gave us a subtle look as if to ask for our silence and attention.

8

Somnambulistic Psychophony

Under the watch-care of a venerated friend, who seemed more like an apostolic figure to us, a poor, demented spirit burst into the room.

He looked like an olden nobleman who had suddenly been pulled from the underground, because the fluids that enveloped him were a truly dark, viscous mass covering his clothing and discharging nauseating emanations.

None of the other suffering spirits had exhibited such a horrendous aspect.

Here and there, on the different faces squeezed together in the place reserved for the afflicted brothers and sisters, the masks of suffering were softened by the unmistakable signs of repentance, faith, humility and hope.

But on this criminal mien, which appeared to have emerged

from a sheet of mud, coldness and malice were combined with astuteness and hardness.

The way he suddenly entered the room caused the other troubled spirits to retreat in fear.

In his right hand, the newly-arrived stranger carried a whip, which he tried to wield while shouting thunderous exclamations.

"Who has forced me to come here against my will?" he bellowed, almost aphonic. "Cowards! Why have you singled me out like this? Where are the vultures that devoured my eyes? Bastards! You shall pay dearly for this affront!"

And displaying his extreme mental unbalance, he continued harshly:

"Who could have known that the damned French Revolution would have repercussions in Brazil? The madness of one people must not cover the whole earth ... The privileges of the nobility are inviolable! They come from kings, who are undisputedly God's chosen! We shall defend our prerogatives; we shall destroy the propaganda of rebels and regicides! I shall sell my slaves who read and write; there shall be no pamphlets or talk of the rebellion. How can they be productive without the lash on their backs? Slaves are slaves, lords are lords. All the fugitives and criminals shall feel the weight of my arms ... I shall kill without mercy. Five whipping posts! Five! That's all I need to restore peace and quiet. "

"He used to be a very cruel plantation owner," explained our friendly guide. "He discarnated during the final days of the 18th century, but he keeps his mind stagnated in the shell of his own selfishness. For the time being, he can perceive nothing but the pictures he has created in his head involving slaves, money and profits from his former rural property. He buried his thoughts there and became the unconscious vampire of the reincarnated souls who were dear to him in colonial Brazil. With all due respect to fraternity, we can say nothing more than the fact that he was a ruthless tormentor of the wretched slaves who fell under his iron glove. A holder of a huge landed estate, he possessed a legion of servants who felt his tyranny and wickedness first hand."

Taking advantage of the brief pause, I gazed at the face of this wretched new arrival with more attention and saw that, although his eyes were moving like those of a cat, they were glassy, lifeless...

I was going to point out those expressionless eyeballs when the instructor, guessing my impulse, added:

"He hated the workers who escaped his claws, and when he could retrieve them from the *quilombos*[8], he not only tied them to the whipping post, but he burned out their eyes, reducing them to blindness as a warning to the others. After being blinded, the few slaves who didn't die from it were sentenced to the jaws of vicious dogs, whose fury they could not escape. Using such a system of repression, he instilled sheer terror around him, thereby amassing fame and fortune. However, the unavoidable trip to the grave overtook him, and in that new phase he met no one but enemies rising beside him in the form of terrible persecutors. Many of his kindhearted victims had forgiven his offenses, but others didn't have the strength for a willing forgiveness and became avengers of the past, inflicting him with torturous dread. Entangled in the web of miserliness, with gold the only power he believed in, he didn't have a clue that he had gone from one mode of life to another through death. He thinks

---

[8] In colonial Brazil, a community organized by fugitive slaves. *Quilombos* were located in inaccessible areas and usually consisted of fewer than 100 people who survived by farming and raiding. The largest and most famous was Palmares, which grew into an autonomous republic and by the 1690s had 20,000 inhabitants. It owed its prosperity to abundant irrigated land and the abduction of slaves from Portuguese plantations. The abducted slaves were kept in bondage by the runaways. Several Portuguese and Dutch slave-hunting expeditions (*bandeiras*) attempted to destroy Palmares; one of these finally succeeded in 1694. www.britannica.com. – Tr.

he is in a dungeon of darkness, tormented by slaves, a prisoner of his own victims. Thus, he lives amid desperation and remorse. Tortured by the memories of the whippings he decreed and hypnotized by tormentors whom he had tortured in the past, he finds himself reduced to complete blindness since the faculties of sight in his perispiritual body are all out of balance."

While we were conversing, the wretch was placed next to Dona Celina.

This struck me unfavorably.

Why would Dona Celina, the best mediumistic instrument in the place, be chosen for this undesirable spirit to communicate?!

I observed her luminous aura – completely the opposite of the pestilential attire of the stranger – and I was overcome with uncontrollable dread.

Wasn't such a measure like handing a fine harp to the paws of a wild beast?

Aulus quickly explained:

"Don't be alarmed. Our demented friend was brought to this center under the supervision and consent of its spirit supervisors. As for his noxious fluids, we don't need to fear them. They instinctively withdraw before the spiritual light that strikes or disintegrates them. That is why each medium possesses his or her own atmosphere, and why each assembly is characterized by a particular magnetic current of self-preservation and defense. Every day, infectious clouds from earth are extinguished or fought by the sun's rays, and troublesome, fluidic formations are destroyed or swept from the planet all the time by the superior energies of the spirit. The luminous rays from a mind oriented to the good descend upon the constructions of evil like electric discharges. Thus, understanding that the best help comes from the most able, our sister Celina is the ideal worker to help him at this time."

Nodding toward her, he said:

"Let's observe."

The medium disengaged from her physical body like someone surrendering to a deep sleep, taking with her the glowing aura that crowned her.

Clementino didn't have to assist her. She seemed to be used to this type of task. Even so, the group's leader kindly supported her anyway.

The noble woman looked at the desperate visitor with obvious sympathy and opened her arms to him, helping him take control of her now-opaque physical vehicle.

As if drawn by a powerful magnet, the suffering spirit flung himself over the medium's physical body, instinctively bonding to her.

Aided by the guardian who had brought him, he sat down with difficulty, seeming to me that he was strongly linked to the mediumistic brain.

While Eugenia had revealed herself to be a worthy nurse, Dona Celina came across like a selfless mother – such was her loving devotion toward her unfortunate guest.

She emitted luminous threads that completely enfolded him, and in light of this, the new-comer, albeit in control of himself, showed that he was being carefully contained by her.

He looked like a fish reacting furiously within the narrow confines of a container that it wants to break out of but can't.

He cast daggers of darkness that vanished in the light with which Celina-spirit gently surrounded him.

He futilely tried to shout insults.

The medium may have been a passive instrument outwardly, but in the depths of her being, she displayed the positive moral qualities that were her unalienable accomplishment, keeping our brother from any undignified manifestation.

"I'm Jose Maria!" shouted the highly irate guest, and then listing a string of other names with the obvious intent of giving importance to his origin.

He piled up claims, gave admonitions and rebelled in exasperation, but I noticed that he wasn't using the same words as before. He seemed constrained, defeated, even though he carried on, rude and coarse.

He seemed so completely, spontaneously and naturally bound to the medium's physiological organization that I couldn't stifle the questions that quickly came to mind.

Was Celina's a different type of speaking mediumship? Eugenia and Celina were both disconnected from their physical bodies while they worked, but why had the former behaved like an apprehensive nurse, while the latter now seemed like a devoted guardian for the demented brother, caring for him like a mother? Why in one a tormented expectation and in the other a serene confidence?

Excusing our condition as learners, Aulus began to enlighten us while Clementino and Raul Silva assisted the communicating spirit through prayers and renewing words, encouraging him toward the good.

"Celina," he kindly explained, "is a perfect somnambulist. In her case, psychophony takes place without the need to connect the nervous system current of the mediumistic brain to the mind of the guest that occupies it. Her spontaneity is such in assigning her resources to spirits in need of help and caring that she has no difficulty in disconnecting automatically from the sensorial field, temporarily losing contact with the motor centers of her brain. Her mediumistic position is one of extreme passivity. Consequently, the communicating spirit can reveal himself more assuredly as he exteriorizes his own personality. This, however, doesn't mean that our sister should be absent or irresponsible. Alongside her body, she acts like a kindly mother assisting the sufferer who is expressing himself through her as if he were a fragile ward of her goodness. She has drawn him to her through a willing self-sacrifice, pleasing to her fraternal heart; and deranged, hapless and spiritually far beneath her, Jose Maria could not resist her. Thus, he is still as aggressive as he always has been, but finds himself restricted in his smallest expressions because in the realms of the spirit, the superior mind subordinates the mind inferior to it. That is why our guest experiences the loving control of the missionary who is providing him fraternal assistance. Compelled to obey her, he receives her constraining mental energies, which oblige him to maintain himself in a respectful attitude, despite his rebelliousness."

During a subsequent pause, we could see that Raul Silva was making progress with his counseling.

The former tyrant was starting to assimilate a few nuggets of light.

Hilario prolonged the lesson by asking:

"Even though she is an invaluable helper, as we can attest, will Dona Celina remember the words the visitor is saying through her?"

"If she wanted to, she could remember them if she tried hard; but in this situation, she would see no advantage in retaining what she hears."

"Obviously," pondered my colleague, "we can see a marked difference between the two mediums when in a trance ... I think that while in the state of conscious psychophony, Dona Eugenia exerted a more direct control over the guest, whereas Dona Celina, although mindful of the communicating spirit, allows him to act more freely ... But if Dona Celina wasn't a capable worker who can immediately put a stop to any unpleasant circumstance, wouldn't Dona Eugenia's faculties be more preferable?"

"Yes, Hilario, you're right. Pure somnambulism, when in careless hands, can produce wonderful phenomena, but it is less useful in the spiritual development of the good. Unconscious psychophony in those who do not possess enough moral merit for their own defense can lead to possession, which only shows up fully in the obsessed who have yielded to its vampirizing forces.

Hilario thought for a moment and then said:

"Here we see a medium outside her physical vessel, mentally controlling the spirit who is morally beneath her ... But ... what if it were the other way around? What if this were an intellectually superior spirit mentally controlling the medium?"

"In that case," Aulus replied patiently, "Celina would be naturally controlled, of course. In such a case, if the communicating spirit were a degenerate and perverse intelligence, the control would fall upon the center's mentors. On the other hand, if it were a messenger with a high degree of knowledge and virtue, the medium would be pleased to yield to it because she would profit from its presence, much like the river is benefited by the rain that falls from above.

The instructor was about to continue, but Clementino asked for his help in removing Jose Maria, who, somewhat renewed, was starting to feel the influence of prayer – even to the extent of reaching the joy of tears.

Our guide went to assist the visitor, who was once again entrusted to the paternal friend who had brought him in order to get him admitted in a distant help organization.

9

Possession

An ailing gentleman in the small group of four people that had come for assistance seemed uncomfortable, afflicted...

He kept saying words that I couldn't quite make out. When asked by Aulus, brother Clementino politely answered:

"Yes, since our work is meant for studying cases like this, we will allow the manifestation."

I realized that our guide was asking for an important demonstration.

We were invited by the instructor to approach the ailing young man, who was supported by a gray-haired woman, his own mother.

In compliance with the supervisor's recommendations, the guards let an obviously deranged spirit abruptly cross the vibratory containment lines, frantically shouting:

"Pedro! Pedro!"

His eyes seemed focused on the patient because he looked at nothing else. When he reached him, our incarnate brother suddenly screamed and collapsed helplessly.

The elderly mother barely had time to break his dramatic fall.

At Clementino's orders, Raul Silva immediately ordered the young man to be transferred to a bed in a nearby room to isolate him from the rest of the assembly.

Dona Celina was put in charge of assisting him.

We accompanied her and the patient with loving interest.

The various tasks continued in the main room without a break in rhythm while we isolated ourselves in the other room to help out with the case.

Pedro and his obsessor now seemed fused with each other.

They were two contestants, grappling in a fierce struggle.

I observed the incarnate spirit more closely and concluded that all the classical symptoms of an epileptic seizure were clearly recognizable.

The patient's face was transfigured by an indefinable paleness; his jaw muscles contracted and his head, displaying clenched teeth, was flexed backward. His arms were like two tree branches blown about by a storm.

Dona Celina and his loving mother helped him into bed and began praying. The rigidity of his body gave way to strange convulsions that reached his eyes, making them roll around without stopping.

The paleness of his face gave way to a reddishness that flushed over his cheeks.

His breathing had become labored, while at the same time his sphincters relaxed. The patient had become a tormented, defeated being.

It was almost as if the insensitive persecutor had entered his victim's body.

He spoke harsh words, which only we could hear, because Pedro's sensory functions had become deplorably inhibited.

As she soothed the patient, Dona Celina sensed the gravity of the illness and she also registered the presence of the wretched visitor; however, she remained alert in order to bravely help him.

I noticed that she was careful not to become passive so that she could follow all the procedures necessary to lend her assistance.

She tried kindly to establish an understanding with the tormenter, but was unable to.

He continued to scream in our ears, without heeding her moving pleas.

"I'll get even! I'll get even! I'll take justice into my own hands!" He screamed in rage.

Offensive accusations vanished in the darkness since they couldn't be exteriorized through the victim's strained vocal cords.

The young man remained completely linked to the tormentor that had suddenly overcome him. His cerebral cortex was enveloped in a dark fluidic mass.

We realized that the young man was incapable of any control over himself.

Caressing his perspiring brow, Aulus said compassionately:

"This is a case of complete possession or essential epilepsy."

"Is our friend unconscious?" asked Hilario between curiosity and respect.

"Yes. Considered a sick man physically, for the time being he has no connections with his physical brain. All the cells of the cortex are suffering the bombardment of toxic magnetic emissions. The motor centers are in disarray. The entire cerebellum is impregnated with noxious fluids. His elements of equilibrium are completely disturbed. For now, Pedro has no means of controlling himself, nor a normal memory for recording this troubling event. This, however, refers only to his dense matter, because in spirit, he is recording all the details of the situation, thereby enriching his storehouse of experiences."

Touched, I observed the sad picture, and with the objective of learning more, I asked:

"Since this is a case involving an incarnate and a discarnate yoked to each other, despite the dreadful condition of their suffering, would it be accurate to consider this to be a mediumistic trance?"

Although involved in the assistance, the instructor answered:

"Yes, this is an epileptic seizure according to terrestrial medicine's usual definition. However, we must regard it as a low level mediumistic trance because we are looking at two imbalanced minds caught in the web of mutual hatred."

And gazing at the pair of convulsing wretches, he added:

"Pedro was in this afflictive situation in the lower zones of the spirit world before being given the blessing of his present reincarnation. For many years, he and his enemy had rolled around in the purgatorial zones in an open duel. Nowadays, their situation has improved. As in many similar cases, their encounters are farther apart. They have given way to the phenomenon we're looking at now since the young man's perispiritual body is still damaged in important areas."

Meanwhile, finding it difficult to reach the obsessor through speech, Dona Celina, with our mentor's help, said an emotional prayer imploring Divine Compassion for the two unfortunate men fighting each other uselessly.

Our venerable friend's words caused her hands to emit streams of luminescent energies that enveloped the two wretches in sensations of relief.

As if he had breathed an anesthetizing substance, the persecutor automatically let go of his victim, who finally fell into a profound and restorative sleep.

Guards and helpers took the half-asleep obsessor to an emergency location.

And while Dona Celina gave a little magnetized water to the patient's weeping and frightened mother, we returned to our cordial conversation.

"In spite of the sickly burden the patient is bearing at the moment, could we say that Pedro is a medium?" asked Hilario attentively.

"Due to the passiveness with which he reflects his discarnate enemy, that would be fair to say, although we must consider that, rather than being a medium in the normal sense of the word, he is an indebted spirit redeeming himself."

"But can he contemplate his own psychic development?"

The Assistant smiled and remarked:

"'To develop' would mean 'to take from the envelope', 'to make progress' or 'to produce'. Understood in those terms, it is reasonable that, before anything else, Pedro must develop personal resources for his own recovery. Solid walls are not built upon an insecure foundation. He will need to heal himself. Then, after that ..."

"If that's the case," interjected my colleague, "won't his coming to this center be pointless?"

"Not at all. He can gather the strength to recover while here, just as a scrawny plant finds a stimulus for its restoration in the fertilizer that it is given. Day by day, in contact with friends guided by the Gospel, Pedro and his foe will incorporate blessed qualities of understanding and service, gradually modifying the state of their mental forces. Their individual development will surface so that the mediumistic faculty may appear later on as crystalline as we would like it to be. Salutary and renewing thoughts assimilated by the pair of sufferers express improvement and recuperation for both, because in their current mutual magnetic connection, the ideas of one react upon the other, thereby causing profound alterations."

In light of our pensive demeanor as we examined such complex issues, the Assistant pondered:

"Valuable mediumistic instruments cannot be made overnight, of course. Like all precious constructions, they require effort, sacrifice, courage and time ... Without love and devotion, the creation of praiseworthy groups and mediums for the tasks of communication with the spirit world would not be possible."

Returning his attention to the sleeping patient, Aulus continued:

"Our friend is under a huge mountain of debt from the past, and no one can freely advance to tomorrow without resolving the commitments of yesterday. That is why Pedro displays an afflictive mediumship of trial. It is the Law that no one can be liberated without paying what is owed. Thus, he must be regarded as a patient who requires care and treatment."

Then, as if he wanted to gather data to complete the lesson, he touched Pedro's forehead, examining it at length.

After a few moments of silence, he said:

"The struggle is rooted in the remote past. We don't have the time to make an in-depth incursion into it, but we can immediately recognize the persecutor of today as the victim of yesterday. In the middle of the last century[9], Pedro was a doctor who abused his healing mission. A detailed mental analysis would catch him in numerous undignified liaisons. The persecutor that presently dominates his energies was his brother, whose wife Pedro sought to seduce. To achieve his aim, he insinuated himself in different ways, in addition to harming his brother both economically and socially until he got him committed to a mental hospital, where he remained for several years, bewildered and useless, waiting for

---

[9] In the middle of the 1800s. – Tr.

death. Upon discarnating and finding his brother with his wife, he went mad with hatred. He battered their lives and waited for them after the grave, where the three were reunited in a dolorous process of regeneration. The less-guilty wife was the first to return to the physical world, where later on she received the morally delinquent doctor as her own son, thereby purifying the love in her soul. The betrayed brother from the past, however, still has not found the strength to change, and obstinate in the hatred to which he thoughtlessly yielded, he continues to vampirize Pedro."

Responding with a friendly look to our expression of amazement, he added:

"We are forced to live in the hell that we create for others so that we may in turn experience the fire with which we afflicted them. No one escapes justice. Reparations may be put off for a while, but they are always inevitable."

The lesson was simple, but the awful situation of the worn-out and sad patient instilled us with justified wonder.

Always eager to learn, Hilario pondered:

"But if Pedro is still a tormented medium, what can he do in a group like this?"

The instructor smiled and responded:

"Chance isn't part of the superior designs. We do not meet each other without reason. Of course, our friend has affective connections from the past here, and it is their duty to help him. If he cannot be a valuable member of the group right away, he can still receive the fraternal assistance indispensable for his full recovery."

"Will he be healed any time soon?" I asked.

"Who knows?" responded Aulus serenely.

And carefully weighing his words, he continued:

"It will depend mostly on him and the victim to whom he is indebted. The assimilation of renewing mental principles leads to a higher vision of life. All the dark dramas of obsession result from a sickly mind. If he applies himself devotedly to his new obligations and if he perseveres in our Consoling Doctrine, he will undoubtedly shorten his expiation, since by converting to the good, he will modify the mental *tonus* of his enemy, who will, in turn, be led to his own renewal through his examples of comprehension and selflessness, humility and faith. Even after the possession episodes end, Pedro will continue to suffer the reflexes of the disequilibrium he brought upon himself. They will show up in the lighter phenomena of secondary epilepsy, which will recur for some time at the mere but strong remembrance of his present struggle, until the readjustment of his perispiritual body is complete."

"And how long will that take?" asked Hilario, somewhat troubled.

Aulus looked thoughtful and replied:

"Who can penetrate someone else's conscience? With the effort of the will, it is possible to hasten the solution to many enigmas and to lessen a lot of pain. The matter, however, is an inner one ... We can rest assured, however, that the seeds of light are never lost. If the mediums that are caught today in dreadful trials persist in creating better destinies, they will become valuable workers in the future that waits for all in blessed reincarnations of spiritual growth and progress."

And in light of our wonder, he concluded:

"The problem is to learn without getting discouraged, and to serve the good without giving up."

10
Tormented Somnambulism

We returned to the main room.

Dona Eugenia had just finished helping a poor recently-discarnated brother, who left the room under the fraternal control of the guards.

We were kindly received by Clementino, who led us over to a young woman who was praying with a distinguished-looking gentleman in the small group of patients receiving assistance that evening.

Caressing her head, Aulus informed:

"We will allow the manifestation of an unfortunate friend who is vampirizing her, not only in order to help him but so that we may learn something about tormented somnambulism."

I watched the young woman who was leaning toward the impeccably dressed man assisting her.

The meeting's supervisor withdrew to oversee other activities, but Aulus took his place and proceeded to explain the case with his characteristic kindness.

Indicating the couple, he said:

"They are husband and wife united in a redemptive trial."

Just then, the spirit guards allowed the unfortunate spirit to enter.

We were face to face with an obviously deranged discarnate.

His dense perispirit bore all the signs of undisputable mental alienation.

He had a vacant look in his eyes, a constricted face, undisguised anxiety...

His presence would inspire repugnance and dread in anyone unaccustomed to caring for the sick.

In addition to a head injury, he had a large ulcer on his throat.

He lunged at the young woman like a big cat lunging at its prey.

She began to scream, transfigured.

However, her spirit had not left her body.

It was she herself who was contorting and weeping convulsively, enveloped in the fluidic embrace of the spirit who had completely taken over her physiological vessel.

Hot tears ran from her half-closed eyes, her body had lost control like a boat at large, and her breathing had become wheezy and labored.

She tried to speak, but her voice was an unpleasant whistle.

Her vocal cords were incapable of articulating one intelligible sentence.

At Clementino's direction, Raul approached the duo in the afflictive encounter and applied magnetic energies to the medium's chest area. She then managed to speak in hoarse shouts:

"Monstrous daughter! ... You're a criminal! ... A criminal! ...

Nothing's going to save you! You will descend with me into the darkness to share my pain ... I don't want any help ... I just want to be with you so you will be with me! I'll never forgive you! I'll never forgive you!"

From convulsive weeping, he incomprehensively began roaring in vengeful laughter.

We couldn't tell if this was a victim lamenting his fate or a sarcastic clown.

"Justice is mine!" he shouted between wheezes. "I'm my own advocate! And vengeance is my only recourse!"

Inspired by his benefactor, Raul tried to renew the tormentor's attitude by speaking to him about the value and advantages of humility, forgiveness, understanding and love.

And while he continued counseling, we looked to our diligent guide.

In answer to our first questions, Aulus pointed out:

"This is a dolorous case like that of thousands of people."

"We can see," exclaimed Hilario, greatly impressed, "that it is our sister herself who is speaking and waving her arms."

"Yes," affirmed the Assistant, "but she is connected to her spirit companion brain to brain."

"Will she be able to clearly recall what is happening?" I asked.

"Not at all. The cells of her cerebral cortex are in complete disarray due to the influence of this unfortunate suffering spirit. In trances where there is a more direct union between her demented persecutor and herself, she falls into a deep hypnosis, like individuals magnetized during a demonstration on hypnotism. Immediately thereafter, she starts displaying his mental imbalances."

And indicating the medium's throat, which had suddenly turned reddish and swollen, he continued:

"On those occasions, her glottis is temporarily altered. She cannot express herself except in a hoarse voice and broken syllables. That is because our tormented brother, to whom she is linked by extremely close ties, transmits his personal sensations to her, forcing her to display his way of being."

"Their association is so entwined," said Hilario, "that I have to ask myself if they might not be two souls in one body, so to speak, like two distinct plants growing in the same pot ... In her daily life, isn't our sister constantly and completely influenced, albeit indirectly, by her obsessing companion?"

"You're on the right track. At home, our friend is an enigma to her family. She is from a prominent background and acquired a wonderful cultural education; her behavior, however, has always been rather shocking, revealing hidden imbalances. At first, she displayed unhappiness and melancholia, which led to nervous breakdowns and circulatory problems. Ill since puberty, renowned doctors tried in vain to diagnose her case until one particular surgeon believed her problem was an imbalance in the thyroid and submitted her to a delicate surgery; but her suffering remained unaltered. Soon thereafter, she met this gentleman, who married her. He was convinced that marriage would be a healthful renewal for her. But her situation grew worse instead. She got pregnant early on in the marriage in accordance with a plan designed in the Greater World. She was to receive her persecutor into her maternal arms to assist in his transformation and to help him find a new destiny. However, sensing his proximity, she recoiled in irrepressible fear, thereby delaying the work she needs to do. Impervious to the suggestions of her own soul, she rebelliously and violently caused a miscarriage. That frustration was the breach that gave her invisible enemy a more extensive influence in her marriage. The poor woman began to suffer frequent conversion disorder, with a sudden aversion to her husband. She is assaulted by phenomena of suffocation and anguish especially at night, grieving her heartbroken mate. Doctors were consulted, but their sedatives were useless ... The demented patient was committed, but insulin and electroshock therapy were ineffective. Presently she's going through a period of rest at home, and her husband has decided to try the help of Spiritism."

While Raul and Clementino attempted to calm the medium and the obsessor, united in a symbiosis of extreme desperation, Hilario and I eagerly sought further clarification.

"What if she became pregnant again?" asked Hilario.

"Yes," Aulus agreed, "that would indeed be a blessing; but because of the web of conflicting sentiments resulting from her trying to escape her responsibilities, she cannot receive such a privilege for now."

I recalled women who had become mothers in insane asylums, but catching my thoughts, Aulus explained:

"Her condition of mental alienation does not deprive her of her natural physical capacities, but her premeditated cruelty in avoiding her commitments has imprinted a certain imbalance on her genital center. Our innermost defections, although unknown by others, harm our perispirit and we cannot rush the time we need to recuperate, even if remorse helps us to restore our good intentions. The perfect interlocking of the psycho-physical elements is associated with the mind. Corporeal life is the synthesis of the soul's radiations. Organs are not in harmony without balanced thoughts, just as there is no order without intelligence."

The spiritual assistance continued apprehensively.

The vengeful spirit yoked to the medium continued to be restrained by Clementino's assistants, while the young woman reflected his emotions and impulses. Her chest heaved and she cried out in tears:

"Nothing will help me ... I'm a renegade!"

"Forgive, my brother, and your pathway will be renewed," replied Raul lovingly. "By forgiving, we ourselves are forgiven. All of us have debts. Wouldn't you like to help others so that you might be helped in turn?"

"I can't, I just can't!" cried the wretch.

And looking at that pair of suffering spirits in one body, Aulus continued to explain:

"In order to calmly examine the anguish of obsession in tormented mediumship, we mustn't forget that the causes of today's suffering are rooted in the shadows of yesterday. Spiritist centers are teeming with moving dramas that are connected to the remote and near past."

Indicating the couple, he continued:

"In the past, her current husband was a harmful companion. He talked her into poisoning her adoptive father, her present persecutor. Heiress to a considerable fortune as a sole adoptive daughter, she found out that her father planned to change his will. This happened in an aristocratic mansion in the last century. The wealthy widower, who had raised her with loving care, did not agree with her choice. He disliked the young man because he seemed more interested in pillaging his wealth than in making the naïve and senseless girl happy. So the father tried to get her away from her fiancé's influence to no avail. Indignant, he was taking legal measures to disinherit her, when the young man exploited her passion for him and talked her into eliminating her father by giving him continuous doses of sedatives. Her old father deteriorated after two weeks of the wrong medication, and his death was achieved with only a minute dose of a corrosive substance. After a brief period of mourning, the young heiress made her new husband rich, but she soon found herself disillusioned. It wasn't long before her husband revealed himself to be a compulsive gambler and confessed libertine, relegating her to profound mental and physical misery. This form of gradual destruction wasn't enough, however. Her discarnate father attached himself to her with a burning desire for revenge, subjecting her to horrible inner torments. On earth, the patricide may have remained concealed, but it was recorded in the divine tribunals, and a long effort of expiation has been in effect, for here and now we are still observing this trio of consciences interlaced in the dilacerating threads of redemptive trial."

The wretched persecutor was taking in Raul's loving admonishing, and after a short break, Aulus continued:

"As we can see, our sister's illness is rooted in the distant past. She roamed around for a long time in the lowest zones of the spirit world in the vibratory field of her victim's hate. Her father had become her vengeful creditor. And now, in her new existence, her mind is entangled with his. She went through childhood and adolescence experiencing his persecution from afar; however, when his enemy from the past reappeared as her current husband with the task of helping and reeducating her, and when she wavered at her first attempt at maternal responsibility, the obsessor took advantage of his magnetic control over her and dashed her equilibrium."

Moved by the picture of justice playing out in front of us, we couldn't avoid asking more questions to better grasp the lesson.

Hilario turned his attention to the victim's loving husband and considered:

"So our friend here has his own debt to pay to his sick wife."

"Undoubtedly," Aulus confirmed gravely. "Divine Power doesn't place at one another's side without a just cause. In marriage, at home or at work, we are sought out through our affinities in order to satisfy the imperatives of the law of love, whether to amplify the good or to redeem our debts resulting from our deliberate contact with evil. Our sister suffers the effects of her crime of patricide resulting from her desire to enjoy pleasures that ended up disrupting her conscience; and the one who inspired that deplorable action has been called on to help her make amends."

I gazed at the downcast gentleman and pondered the frustration he must be feeling.

That was enough for Aulus to explain solicitously:

"Of course, our friend is not at all happy. Recapitulating his old desire for sensations, he re-approached the woman he married, instinctively seeking the partner of his passionate venture of the past; instead, he found the sick sister, who makes him ponder and suffer."

"Examining this case for our studies," said Hilario, "can we still regard her as a medium?"

"Why not? She is a medium undergoing an afflictive process of readjustment. She will probably be a patient in need of love and care for a few more years. Imprisoned in the fluidic web of her demented adversary, she is purifying herself by means of the complications of tormented somnambulism. Thus, for now she is an instrument for the development of patience and goodwill in this group of workers, but without any perspective of immediate production in the area of assistance; after all, she is in extreme need of fraternal assistance herself."

"But even now," I added, "her presence here is not useless."

"Not in the slightest," added the instructor. "First of all, she and her husband are a valuable focus of work, enabling our fellow co-workers to improve their qualities as sowers of the light. In addition, the impact of the counseling is not lost. From evening to evening, from meeting to meeting, in the intimacy of prayer and constructive counseling, our trio of souls will renew themselves bit by bit. The persecutor will understand the need to forgive in order to get better, the patient will strengthen herself in spirit for her recovery, and the husband will acquire patience and serenity in order to be truly happy."

At this point, with the help of the center's spirit friends, the obsessor was removed from the psychic environment of the young woman, who returned to normal. In answer to our questioning look, Aulus remarked:

"When our brother Clementino invited us to observe this case, he undoubtedly wanted to highlight the imperatives of work and tolerance, understanding and kindness for the building of wholesome mediumship in the world. Mediums are found everywhere, but few of them have freed themselves from their somber past to serve the common cause of humankind in the present, without the enigmas of their particular pathway. And since no one advances with all possible serenity without paying the debts left behind, we must tolerate and help, edifying through good deeds."

Our conversation was suddenly interrupted.

Clementino, ever diligent, called us to help out with another case.

11
An Out-of-Body Task

Now it was medium Antonio Castro's turn.

Profoundly concentrated, he displayed all the confidence with which he offered himself to the objectives of the work at hand.

Brother Clementino approached him and like a regular magnetizer, began applying longitudinal passes[10] to him.

Antonio slowly fell asleep; his arms and legs became rigid.

An abundance of a whitish mist emanated from the medium's chest area, and accumulating like a cloud to the left of his dense body, it soon became a somewhat larger- sized duplicate of it.

Antonio seemed more highly developed, presenting all the particularities of his physical form but noticeably expanded.

I wanted to ask a few questions, but the solemnity of the work kept me quiet.

---

[10] See Ch. 17 for more detail. – Tr.

The center's spiritual director was subjecting the medium to a delicate magnetic procedure that ought not be disturbed or interrupted.

Disconnected from his corporeal vehicle, Antonio took two steps away from it, enabling us to see the vaporous cord that kept him connected to the somatic field.

While his inert physical body rested, he appeared before us, fumbling and surprised as a strange replica of himself: besides appearing larger, his right side was bluish in color, whereas his left was orangey.

He tried to move but seemed to feel heavy and restless.

Clementino repeated the magnetic procedures, and Antonio, out of his body, withdrew somewhat, as if to juxtapose himself on his physical body.

I realized that this contact produced a notable difference: the corporeal body had instinctively swallowed certain bands of energy that caused an obvious irregularity in his perispirit, absorbing them in a manner incomprehensible to me.

The medium, still outside his dense body, took on his normal appearance.

He was now himself without any distortion. He was light and agile, although he remained bound to his physical envelope through the aeriform cord, which seemed thinner and more luminous as Antonio-spirit moved about.

While Clementino encouraged him with friendly words, Aulus noticed our curiosity and explained:

"With the supervisor's assistance, the medium has been properly exteriorized. At first, his perispirit or 'astral body' was clothed in the vital effluvia that ensure the equilibrium between the soul and the corporeal body. These effluvia together are known as the 'etheric double', formed by neuro-psychic emanations that belong to the physiological field. For that reason, these emanations cannot achieve a greater separation from the physical body, slated as they are for disintegration, as happens to the corporeal vessel, at the time of renewing death. To better adjust to our ambient, Antonio has returned those energies to his motionless body, thereby ensuring the necessary warmth to its cells, as well as disencumbering himself as much as possible to do the work that awaits him."

"Ah!" exclaimed Hilario in wonder, "so this is the exteriorization of sensitivity[11]!"

"Yes. If a human researcher were to strike the area where the medium's perispirit is located, Antonio would immediately register the pain of the blow and would complain about it using his physical mouth, because, although free of the somatic vehicle, he is still in communion with it through the fluidic tie."

I closely observed the medium's perispirit, which was now in the realm of our circle of work.

He was not wearing the blue and grey outfit that dressed his physical body, but a one-piece white robe that went from his shoulders down to the floor, hiding his feet. He moved about in a gliding manner.

Aulus perceived my inner observations and explained:

"With Clementino's help, our brother is utilizing his own ectoplasmic capabilities, strengthened by resources from our environment. Such energies exude from our soul according to the specific density of our body, varying from the sublime fluidity of luminescent radiations to the pasty substance that operates the varied phenomena of metamorphosis in chrysalises."

After watching the hesitant medium for a few moments, he continued:

"Antonio is still a novice at this kind of endeavor. As he gains more experience, he will be able to handle advanced mental

---

[11] Sensory power of the medium outside the periphery of the body. www.spiritwritings.com. – Tr.

possibilities, taking on whatever appearance he wishes. The perispirit is composed of malleable elements that obey the command of the thought, whether it arises from our own imagination or the imagination of minds stronger than ours, especially when our will thoughtlessly surrenders to the domination of tyrannical or wicked spirits dwelling in the darkness."

"So, if he could, Antonio ..." Hilario began curiously.

Cutting him short, the Assistant finished for him:

"If he could think firmly while outside the physical field, and if he had already gained a good degree of self-control, he would easily imprint the image he wanted on the pliable energies that envelop him, appearing before us anyway he wished. It is possible to imprint on ourselves the appearance that we would like to have."

"Yet," I pondered, "it is important to realize that such appearance, albeit alive, is not comparable to the clothing on our plane."

Aulus perceived that my questions always included the need for greater clarification for Hilario. He was still a novice in our field of activity and perhaps that is why Aulus tried to answer as clearly and as detailed as possible:

"Not in the least. Our thoughts mold the form we are inclined to adopt; however, the means of our presentation in the different realm of life into which we were brought – as you already know – varies in its diverse types. Let's take a tattooed man as an example. He might have chosen a design that, for some time, makes his form easily recognizable, but he will wear garments that are closest to his taste, according to the customs of his social environment."

And smiling, he added:

"Through mental concentration, any spirit can present itself in any way it so desires. Nonetheless, by using our creative imagination, we can and should mobilize the resources within our reach to improve artistic conceptions in our relationships with one another. Art, as well as science, is much richer in our sphere than in the circle of incarnates, and through art, education is processed more efficiently as far as beauty and culture are concerned. Thus, as we cannot conceive of a dignified and noble earthly society composed solely of men and women in complete nudity – even with fine tattoos – it is necessary to remember that individuals in our community, despite having a vehicle prodigiously sculpted by mental powers, do not disparage fine clothing with which we express different emotions and distinct manners. We mustn't forget that progress is an educational endeavor. The ascent of the spirit could not be a regress to the empiricism of the tribal life."

Aulus became silent.

The medium, now more at ease outside his dense physical body, was receiving Clementino's fatherly instructions.

Two assistants placed a helmet over his head in the form of a blinder.

"For the trip he is about to take," Aulus said, "Antonio must not get distracted. He is new at this type of task and needs suitable means to reduce his ability to see so that it may interfere as little as possible while the task is being performed."

At this point, the young man was completely outside his body and was rising in space, holding the hands of both assistants.

As we looked on expectantly, the trio volitated at an oblique angle.

Showing that he was still in close communion with his physical body, we heard him speak through his physical mouth:

"We are going along a dark and narrow path! ... Oh, I'm afraid, I'm very afraid! ... Rodrigo and Sergio are supporting me, but I'm afraid! ... I have the impression that we're in a thick fog..."

Showing signs of anguish and strangeness, he continued:

"What sort of night is this? ... The darkness weighs on us! ... Woe is me! ... I can see unknown forms moving beneath our feet! I want to go back! Go back! ... I can't go on! ... I can't do it! I can't!"

However, inspired by the center's spirit mentor, Raul raised the vibratory level of the group with a fervent prayer, beseeching the higher spheres to give Antonio strength.

Aulus explained:

"The group's prayer, accompanying him and transmitted to him as he proceeds, will act immediately like a blessed spiritual tonic."

"Ah! Yes, my friends!" continued Antonio, as if his physical body were a radio receiver for communicating from far away, "your prayer is acting on me like a shower of light ... Thank you for this benefit! ... I feel comforted! ... I shall press on!"

Interpreting the facts we were observing, the Assistant explained:

"Few incarnate spirits achieve complete control over themselves on journeys of spiritually edifying service outside their dense bodies. Accustomed to orienting themselves with their physical body, when facing any unpleasant occurrence in the realm of unusual phenomena, they instinctively try to return to it, like the mollusk seeking refuge in its shell when it experiences anything in disaccord with its routine movements. Antonio, however, will be trained to lend invaluable assistance to patients of all sorts."

As we listened to these remarks, the medium's voice rose in the air, strong and clear.

"What a relief! ... We have broken through the barrier of darkness! ... The atmosphere is bathed in a light fragrance! ... The stars are shining again ... Oh! It's a city of light ... Shining spires are reaching for the sky! We're entering a large park! Oh, my

God! Who is that smiling at me? ... It's Oliveira! How different he looks! So much younger; so much, much younger ..."

Copious tears bathed the medium's face, moving all of us.

With a gesture of someone surrendering to a loving, heart-to-heart embrace, the medium continued:

"What bliss! What bliss! Oliveira my friend, I've missed you so much! ... Why have we been without your assistance? We know that the Lord's Will must be done, but your absence has been a torment for us! ... The memory of your love is alive and well at our center ... Your work is an unforgettable example of Christian love! ... Please come to us! Encourage us to sow the good! Dear friend, we know that death is life itself, but we miss you!"

The traveler's voice, heard from so far away, was now broken from time to time by sobs of grief.

Raul, too, was moved to tears.

Aulus explained what was happening:

"Oliveira was a selfless worker in this sanctuary of the Gospel. He discarnated a few days ago, and with the consent of the guides, Antonio has been taken to him to transmit the group's affectionate greetings. Oliveira is recuperating and is still incapable of a more intimate communication with those he left behind. But he can send a message through Antonio."

"Embrace me; yes, dear friend!" continued Antonio with an indescribable inflexion of fraternal warmth. "I'm ready! ... I'll communicate to them whatever you want to say ... Speak and I'll repeat it!"

Assuming the position of someone who must act like a worthy intermediary, his facial expression changed and began speaking rhythmically to the group:

"Dear friends, may the Lord repay you. I'm doing fine, but I'm convalescing, incapable of a more difficult journey ... I feel comforted, almost blissful! Of course, I do not deserve these blessings, for I am in the Grand Home, assisted by unforgettable and sublime affections! The prayers of our group reach me every evening as a projection of flowers and blessings! How can I express my gratitude if the earthly word is always insufficient for defining the great sentiments of our lives? May the Father reward you! ... Here, where I am now, I have once again realized my little worth, and that all of our sacrifices for the cause of the good are mere trifles when compared to the munificence of the Divine Goodness! My friends, charity is the great path! Let us work! ... May Jesus bless us!"

Antonio's voice went silent. A few minutes later, we saw him returning to the meeting, helped by the two assistants. He easily retook his body.

Readjusting himself as his body reabsorbed him, Antonio Castro suddenly awoke in the corporeal realm, in possession of all his normal faculties. He rubbed his eyes as if he had awakened from a deep sleep.

The out-of-body task was over, and through it we had received a valuable lesson.

12
Clairvoyance and Clairaudience

I could see that the meeting was coming to end.

Two highly profitable hours had flown by.

Raul Silva looked at his watch and informed the group that it was time for the closing prayers.

The suffering spirits in the room would receive vibrations of help through the prayer, while the members of the group would recoup their own energies.

A small glass pitcher of fresh water was brought to the table.

When Hilario asked if we were going to witness some sort of special ceremony, the Assistant explained affably:

"No, not at all. The water is going to be magnetized. The plain liquid will be infused with highly beneficial magnetic properties for the participants' psychophysical equilibrium."

In fact, as soon as we heard the explanation, Clementino

approached the pitcher, and with prayerful thoughts, he slowly began to be crowned with light.

With his right hand over the pitcher, luminous particles were projected over the clear liquid, which absorbed them completely.

"Magnetized water," continued Aulus, "can have a valuable medicinal effect. There are lesions and deficiencies in the perispirit reflected in the physical body that only a magnetic intervention can alleviate until those affected promote their own healing."

Aulus became silent while Silva asked the mediums to watch and listen carefully for any instructions that might be ministered to the group that evening by the center's spirit friends.

We saw that Celina, Eugenia and Antonio Castro sharpened their attention.

After he had prepared the medicinal water, Clementino focused on the three more particularly by applying passes to their frontal area.

"Our friend," clarified Aulus, "is trying to aid the mediums by enhancing their sensorial field. For the time being, their clairvoyance and clairaudience shouldn't be too heightened. In the sphere of reincarnated spirits, we have to gauge these experiences so that we don't harm the imperatives of order. Each one of us must be on his or her level of service, doing the best we can. Let's imagine, for example, a radio picking up every type of wavelength all at the same time. The usefulness and harmony of the transmission would be truly impracticable, and there wouldn't be any constructive purpose in the message. Thus, mediums should not dwell on all the occurrences of the ambient they are in, lest they throw their own impressions off balance. Exception is made when, because of their own advancement, mediums are in control of their working field to the point where they can dominate the influences of the environment and select them according to the high criterion of those who can already direct themselves toward the good and also direct those who accompany them."

Hilario thought for a moment and asked:

"So is mediumship basically the same for all three mediums?"

"Not at all. The sphere of perception varies in each of us. There are different kinds of mediumship; however, we must realize that each spirit lives at a certain degree of mental development, and thus the results of mediumistic efforts differ from individual to individual, just as the meanings of life differ from soul to soul. The mediumistic faculties may be identical in different individuals, but each person has his or her own particular way of using them. A large group of artists can be looking at the same model, yet each one will set the model to canvas in his or her own way. A lamp will emit a continuous lily-white light, but if this same light is projected through multiple filters, it will take on the color and potential of each one, even though the light is still the same light. Mediumship entails affinity and filtration. Each spirit lives amid the energies it is attuned to, transmitting them according to the concepts that characterize its way of being."

Observing the care that brother Clementino employed in preparing the mediums, Hilario asked further:

"Are clairvoyance and clairaudience localized solely in the eyes and ears of the incarnate individual?"

Aulus patted Hilario's head and pointed out:

"Hilario, I can see that you are just beginning your journey of higher understanding. Physical eyes and ears are to seeing and hearing what glasses are to the eyes and hearing aids to the ears – merely supplementary devices. All perception is mental. If properly trained, incarnate deaf and blind individuals can hear and see through means different than those commonly used. Hertz waves and X-rays are teaching human beings that there are sounds and light way beyond their limited vibratory frontiers, and mediums are individuals gifted with special neuro-psychic abilities that extend beyond the horizon of their senses."

Hilario nodded that he had grasped the lesson so far, and continued respectfully:

"However, I would like to know if Dona Celina, for example, is seeing and hearing brother Clementino solely through the perception proper on earth."

"Yes, that is the case because of habit. Celina thinks she is hearing the spirit supervisor through her auditory channels, and she believes she is seeing him as if the photographic equipment of her eyes were functioning in connection with the center of her memory. However, this is a consequence of habit. Even in the area of common impressions, people may use their eyes and ears but they actually see and hear with their brain. And in spite of the brain using the cells of the cortex to select the sounds it hears and to imprint the images it sees, it is actually the mind that does it. All the senses in the physiological realm belong to the soul, which fixes them in the physical body according to principles established for the evolution of spirits reincarnated on the earth."

Smiling, he added:

"You have proof of this when people are naturally 'out-of-body' each night during sleep, seeing and hearing, despite the inactivity of the eyes and ears, in what they call 'dream life'."

And lowering his voice, he added:

"We are receptors of reduced capacity in the midst of the innumerable forms of energy flung at us by all the realms of the universe, capturing only a mere fraction of them. In sum, our mind is a limited spiritual dot developing in knowledge and love in the infinite and glorious spirituality of God.

A few more instants went by.

"Let's focus our attention on prayer to prepare ourselves to serve the good!"

Clementino was speaking in a clear, slow voice as if offering a single point for the convergence of our thoughts.

Attentive to the purposes of our study, however, I saw the mediums more directly interested in this appeal.

Dona Celina registered his words precisely, like a disciplined student.

Dona Eugenia assimilated them intuitively, like a discerning learner.

Antonio, however, didn't register them at all.

With Aulus's permission, we began our analysis.

I observed that, subtly tied to Clementino's fluidic wavelength, each of the three mediums sensed his presence in his or her own way.

Dona Celina registered his smallest movements, like a student before her teacher. Dona Eugenia noted his proximity less clearly, as if she saw him imperfectly through a sheet of mist, and Antonio, although he could see him clearly, seemed to be aloof to the instructor's influence.

"For now, Celina's and Antonio's clairvoyant and clairaudient abilities are more extensive than sister Eugenia's," Aulus explained. "All three are lightly subject to Clementino's magnetic command and can recognize his presence in analogous ways because, in the circumstances in which they operate, they are acting like ordinary persons using their normal senses."

"But if the three of them are all under the supervisor's magnetic command," asked Hilario, "why is it that the two women have registered his invitation, whereas Antonio is visibly impervious to it?"

"The center's mentor exerts only a gentle influence and avoids any stronger pressure that could cause a magnetization that would be harmful to our friends. Also, Antonio's mind has subtly begun to nourish different purposes. Unable to focus his attention on the higher spheres of the endeavor to be accomplished, at this point he is no longer interested in Clementino's aims; he wants a meeting with his discarnate mother, instead. He sees Clementino as someone who just doing his job, but who is not concerned about listening to the person or being of real service because his emotions are focused on his domestic circle for now. Antonio's mental indifference is such that he isn't attuned to the current interests of the collective effort of the meeting."

Evidently wanting to shed more light on the lesson within the framework of our earthly knowledge, he added:

"He's like an antenna that has suddenly become non-responsive, refusing to tune into the wavelength that seeks it."

Just then, we saw a likeable fellow from our plane approach the circle of participants and speak to Celina discreetly.

She heard his voice, but didn't turn around. However, she did respond to him in thought, in words that we could hear perfectly well: "We shall meet later."

Aulus informed us:

"It's our sister's discarnate husband. He has a loving request in mind. However, Celina is so disciplined that she can forego the comfort of hearing him so that she can contribute more surely to the success of tonight's meeting."

Soon thereafter, we saw Antonio once again out of his body, this time supported only by the strong desire to leave the group. Covered in the emanations that disfigured his perispirit, he walked hesitantly toward a friendly spirit waiting for him a short distance away.

"Our coworker," said the Assistant, "is less accustomed to edifying discipline and thinks he has done enough for the assistance planned for this evening. He has gone after his mother, who is being helped by our organization."

There was no more time for more questions.

Clementino, at the head of the assembly, raised his arms in a posture of prayer.

Scintillations of sapphirine splendor covered his chest area, giving us the impression that the selfless benefactor had turned into a wingless angel.

A few moments later, a true outpouring of solar light descended from the Higher Spheres to crown his brow. His hands began radiating a prodigious fount of light that reached us all, incarnates and discarnates alike, filling us with a sensation of indescribable well-being.

I couldn't say a word in spite of the questions flooding my mind.

The mentor's rapture compelled us to respectful silence.

Those minutes of vibrations without words represented a precious fountainhead of restorative energies to anyone who opened the gates of the spirit to them.

That was what I could perceive by the reinvigoration of my own energies.

Once the unforgettable procedure was over, Raul asked for a few more moments of tranquility and expectation.

The group was now to wait for the manifestation of any of the center's spirit guides who might bring a general instruction to close the meeting.

Dona Celina asked permission to tell everyone that she had seen a crystalline stream in the room, in whose waters many patients were bathing themselves. Dona Eugenia came next, stating that she had perceived a building filled with children singing hymns of praise to God.

We were very surprised by such statements.

We hadn't seen anything that would remotely remind us of a stream of healing waters or a pavilion for children.

The room was too small to allow for such scenarios.

Looking at me questioningly, Hilario seemed to be wondering if the two mediums might not be under the influence of some momentary disturbance.

Aware of our surprise, Aulus replied attentively:

"We must remember that both were connected to Clementino's magnetic wavelength, picking up the images that his mind suggested to them. They saw his thoughts relating to assisting the sick and a school that the institution plans to build in the near future to aid brothers and sisters. Ideas carefully crafted generate forms, infused with movement, sound and color, perfectly perceptible to all those who are in tune with their wavelength. We mustn't forget that there are phenomena of clairvoyance and clairaudience that derive from the active observation of the mediums, identifying people, places and things outside themselves, much like what happens in ordinary earthly perceptions. And then there are others that derive from the suggestions brought to them by the creative thoughts of discarnate and incarnate friends. These are stimuli that the mind of each medium translates according to his or her abilities, thus resulting in highly diverse interpretations."

"Ah!" replied Hilario enthusiastically, "that is what obsessors do when they create various hallucinatory impressions for their victims."

"Yes, exactly," confirmed the Assistant. "But let's forego any further considerations right now. The meeting is about to end."

13
Thought and Mediumship

A profound and respectful silence had set in.

The group was awaiting the closing message.

I felt that the ambient was lighter, more pleasant.

A brilliant band of light appeared over Dona Celina's head. She became ecstatic, completely disengaged from her physical body and surrounded by bluish radiations.

Surprised by this beautiful phenomenon, I gave Aulus a questioning look. He quickly explained.

"Our sister Celina is going to transmit the words of a benefactor who, although not present in this space, will communicate with us through teledynamic fluids connecting him to the medium's mind."

"That's possible?" asked Hilario discreetly.

Aulus responded:

"Take radio and television, for instance. A person can hear and see another person in a different city if both of them are perfectly attuned via the same wavelength. Celina is familiar with the sublime forces that envelop her and trustfully surrenders to them, assimilating the mental current that seeks her cooperation. She will communicate the lesson automatically, as occurs in somnambulistic psychophony, because the spirit mentor has found her brain cells and nervous system energy akin to the well-tuned keys of a harmonious piano."

The Assistant suddenly became quiet, fixing his gaze on the abundant outpouring of sapphirine light that reached every corner of the room.

I looked at the participants.

The medium's face reflected a mysterious bliss unbeknownst on earth.

Her rapture seemed to have spread to everyone present.

I wanted to make a few remarks, but the Assistant touched me lightly, reminding me to be quiet and respectful.

Dona Celina's modified voice then resounded clearly and movingly, more or less in these terms:

"Dear friends," began the instructor, who had been following our work from afar, "let us keep the peace that Jesus has bequeathed us so that we may serve him in peace.

"With regard to mediumship, let us not overlook our thoughts.

"The soul lives where the mind is.

"We will progress at the influx of our own creations, wherever they might be.

"Gravitation in the mental field is as incisive as it is in the realm of physical experience.

"By serving the overall progress, the soul moves in the glory of the good; by encasing itself in selfishness, it drags itself around, unbalanced, in the darkness of evil.

"The Divine Law is the Good of All.

"To take part in carrying out its wise purposes is to illuminate the mind and to purify life. To impose obstacles on it under the pretext of cherishing pernicious whims is to darken the mind and to congeal the darkness around ourselves.

"It is necessary to assess the direction of our lives in order to avoid the clouds of disturbance and the pain of remorse.

"In the realms of the spirit there is no neutral ground.

"We evolve with the eternal light according to God's designs, or we stagnate in the darkness according to the undue determination of the 'self'.

"It is not enough to simply incarnate or discarnate, since every day forms are made and unmade.

"What counts is inner renewal with an increased purpose, so that we progress with the right notion of the eternity in which we move throughout time.

"A conscience that is heavy with evil purposes, covered with remorse, filled with unrestrained ambitions or darkened with afflictions cannot help but attract similar forces that chain it to infernal turmoil.

"Obsession is the sinister union of the mind with the imbalance typical of the darkness.

"We think, and thus we give life to the object ideated.

"The visible result of our innermost thoughts reveals our spiritual condition, and those who are in tune with the nature of our inclinations and desires draw near to us through the thoughts we emit.

"If we linger in the lowest spheres of the human experience, those who are still wandering about in animality will seek us out, attracted by the character of our inferior impulses, absorbing the mental substances we emit, and projecting their own characteristics upon us.

"To imagine is to create.

"All creation has life and movement, however brief, laying responsibility on the conscience that manifests it. And since life and activity are tied to the principles of exchange, it is indispensable to analyze what we give in order to assess what we should receive in return.

"Those who mentalize only anguish and crime, misery and disturbance, what other images can they reflect in the mirror of their own soul but those of disharmony and suffering?

"Wicked individuals in the presence of saints would not recognize their purity, since feeding on their own emanations they would see nothing but their own darkness.

"Those who only look for rocks on the road will certainly find more than just inconsequential little pebbles.

"Those who linger indefinitely measuring the depth of the mud are in danger of drowning in it.

"The traveler who is fascinated by the briers along the road runs the risk of going mad amongst the thorns of the wild bushes.

"Let us watch our thoughts, purifying them in the incessant work of the good in order to rid ourselves of the shackles capable of chaining us to dark processes of inferior purposes.

"It is from the living forge of thought that the wings of the angels and the chains of the condemned emerge.

"By means of thought, we enslave ourselves to the posts of infernal suffering, at times sentencing ourselves to centuries of wandering on the paths of pain and death.

"Tormented mediumship is nothing more than the entwining of souls compromised in afflictive trials, in the midst of readjustment.

"To shorten the torment that punishes the expiating incarnate or discarnate conscience in a thousand different ways, mental renewal is indispensable. It is the only means for the recovery of harmony.

"As for religion, being satisfied merely with the religious label without making any effort at inner sublimation is as dangerous to the soul as possessing an honorary designation and disdaining its intrinsic responsibility would be to the incarnate person.

"Titles of faith are not mere words, covering our deficiencies and weaknesses. They express duties of spiritual growth that we cannot run from without harming our obligations.

"In our circles of activity, therefore, it is not sufficient to merely believe and to persuade.

"No one is truly worthy of being called a Spiritist simply for having been healed of a persistent skin disease with the aid of friendly spirits and consequently deciding to accept the intervention of the spirit world in his or her life. Likewise, no one is a medium – in the lofty meaning of the word – solely because he or she is the instrument of communication between visible and invisible beings.

"To earn the position in the work we are destined to perform according to the higher principles that ennoble our path, we must implement their essence in our lives through the testimony of our conversion to sanctifying love.

"Thus, it is not enough to simply ponder the grandeur of our higher idealism. We have to materialize its loftiness in our day-to-day lives.

"Great artists can put the spark of genius in a mere brush stroke, a small block of marble or the smallest musical piece. Souls that are truly converted to Christ reflect his beauty in the smallest gestures of each hour, whether in the utterance of a few words, in secret aid on behalf of their neighbors, or in the silent selflessness that remains unknown to the world.

"Our thoughts engender our actions, and our actions engender thoughts in others.

"Let us inspire sympathy and spiritual growth, worthiness and goodness around us so that we will not lack the precious bread of happiness tomorrow.

"Being certain of our immortality without improving our immortal spirit is like shining a light in the desert.

"Mediation between two different planes without moral growth is to stagnate in uselessness.

"Thought is as important for mediumship as the riverbed is important for the river. Run pure waters over a riverbed of putrid mud and you will have only the resulting dark current of sludge.

"Of course, divine messages will descend from heaven to earth, but for that to happen, it is imperative to build suitable channels.

"Jesus is waiting for the formation of human messengers capable of projecting the marvels of his Kingdom into the world.

"To reach this ideal stage, it is crucial for those who have psychic faculties not to dwell simply in communicating with spirits. They must consecrate their energies to the highest expressions of life, seeking the material to pave their own pathway by educating themselves and selflessly serving their neighbor.

"Communing with the guides of the earth's spiritual progress through books, we enrich ourselves with knowledge and we increase our mental abilities; and continuously sowing the good produces a harvest of sympathy, without which the silo of life is reduced to a den of desperation and discouragement.

"It is not enough to see, to hear or to channel discarnate spirits in order to become a respectable individual.

"Ignorant or irresponsible brothers and sisters naturally swarm every corner of the earth due to the deficient evolutionary condition of the planet's collectivities. Quite often, without any roots in perversity per se, thousands of discarnate souls practice vampirism on unvigilant incarnates simply to continue enjoying the sensations of the physical realm, sensations they lack the courage to leave behind.

"Every task, in order to grow, requires workers that are dedicated to their own growth.

"This is obvious in every realm of nature.

"There is no fruit on a budding tree.

"Uncut wood cannot be used effectively in the household.

"Shifting sands do not ensure a firm foundation.

"There is no light in a lamp without oil.

"A car cannot run smoothly where the pickax has not yet opened a road.

"How can we expect divine thought where human thought is set on the lower considerations of life?

"What messenger of heaven will make the celestial message illuminate our understanding when the mirror of our soul remains darkened by the lowest interests?

"A star would try in vain to reflect itself in the mire of a bog.

"Friends, let us be mindful of the good and do it.

"Everything that exists in nature is an exteriorized idea.

"The universe is the projection of the Divine Mind, and the earth, the way you know it in its political and social context, is a product of the human mind.

"Civilizations and peoples, cultures and experiences comprise forms of thought through which we incessantly evolve toward the higher spheres.

"So let us heed the duty of self-improvement.

"Without understanding and kindness, we will join the wretched offspring of rebelliousness.

"Without study and observation, we will dwell forever among the unfortunate exponents of ignorance.

"Love and wisdom are the wings that will launch our definitive flight toward perfect communion with the Heavenly Father.

"Let us ascend to the higher realms, instilling thoughts of sublimation in those around us.

"Speech enlightens.

"Example captivates.

"Let us conform ourselves to the redemptive Gospel.

"Jesus Christ is the aim of our self-renewal.

"By regenerating our lives according to his standards, we will restructure the inner lives of those around us.

"My friends, believe!

"Pure and active thought is the force that drives us from hatred to love, from pain to joy, from earth to heaven...

"Let us seek Jesus' consciousness so that our own may portray his perfection and beauty!

"Let us learn to reflect his glory and love so that the heavenly light may spread over souls, just as the sun's splendor extends over the entire world.

"Let us begin our effort of spiritual renewal today, and tomorrow we will have advanced considerably on the great path!

"My friends, my brothers and sisters, praying that Jesus continues to sustain us all, I leave you with a 'see you soon'."

The medium's voice became still.

Very moved, we saw that the brilliant outpouring above us had ceased.

Raul Silva said a short prayer to close the meeting.

We bid Clementino goodbye.

"Come back anytime," he invited us graciously.

Yes, yes, we would continue to further our studies.

We left happily with Aulus as if we had sipped the living water of peace from the cup of bliss.

14
In Spiritual Service

We were heading away from the Spiritist center when Dona Celina's discarnate husband, who we had seen during the meeting, approached us.

He seemed to know Aulus because he stopped next to us and said:

"My dear Assistant, a moment please."

Aulus introduced him:

"This is our brother Abelardo Martins. He was Celina's husband and has been adapting himself to the way we carry out our activities."

We could see right away that Abelardo was not an evolved spirit. His manners and speech revealed the spiritual state of someone still deeply attached to earthly habits.

"My dear Assistant," he continued nervously, "I have come to ask for help for Liborio. The group's assistance has improved his disposition, but now his wife has gotten worse. She doesn't leave him alone."

"You can count on us," Aulus readily replied, "but we're going to need Celina's help."

And patting him on the shoulder, he concluded:

"Go back to Celina for now. As soon as she disengages from her body through sleep, bring her with you, so that we can proceed together. We'll be waiting in the nearby garden."

Abelardo left happily as we entered an enormous tree-covered plaza.

While we were waiting, Aulus used the time to comment on Abelardo's request:

"Abelardo is worried about Liborio dos Santos, the first spirit that communicated this evening through Dona Eugenia."

Extending his explanation, he told us that Dona Celina's husband had been wandering around in despair for a long time.

During his physical life he was temperamental and had not been able to resign himself to the imperatives of death right away.

Headstrong and irascible, he discarnated very early from excesses that damaged his organic strength.

He tried in vain to obsess his wife as if she were a mere servant.

When he realized he couldn't vampirize her, he spent a few years in the realms of darkness amid rebellious and irreverent spirits until the prayers of his wife, aided by the intercession of many friends, were able to alter his mind.

Finally, he yielded to the facts.

Abelardo acknowledged the impropriety of his mental intemperance, and after being suitably prepared by the group of friends at the center, he was admitted to an assistance organization, where he started to serve as a warder of imbalanced brothers and sisters.

As soon as the Assistant finished this brief biography, Hilario asked:

"The contact with Abelardo raises interesting questions ... For instance, will he continue in communion with his wife?"

"Yes. Their love is deeply rooted in the past."

"In spite of their differences?"

"Why not? Does the Heavenly Father stop loving us because of our faults?

"Indeed," agreed Hilario, a bit disappointed, "that is indisputable. "However, has Abelardo reconnected with his wife?"

"Completely. He finds in her an invaluable incentive for his current self-recovery."

"But as a discarnate spirit, does he actually share her home?"

"As much as he can. Because he gave in to indiscipline and disturbance, he still suffers the disagreeable consequences of the imbalance he surrendered to. That is why his earthly home and his wife's tenderness are the greatest paradise he can enjoy for now. He dedicates himself daily to the arduous service of assisting demented spirits, but he rests, whenever possible, at home next to his wife. Once a week he accompanies her in prayer at home; He is closely associated to her mediumistic endeavors; and every evening, when circumstances allow, both dedicate themselves to assisting the ill. They were not only husband and wife in earthly terms. They are infinitely good friends, and Abelardo is now trying to make good use of the time for readjustment. He dreams of the moment when, changed for the better, he will receive Celina when she returns to the spirit world."

"Is that common? Is the separation of couples only imaginary?"

"One case does not make a rule," Aulus responded good-humoredly. "Where there is no affinity of sentiments, the earthly marriage is a redemptive endeavor and nothing more. In most situations, death only confirms a separation that already existed in everyday life. In such cases, the spouse leaves the physical body after his or her trial, like a debtor who has found peace after having paid everything off. However, when the ties of the soul rise above the emotions of the human journey, even in the case where the surviving spouse marries a second time, the spiritual communion continues sublimely in a loving and constant exchange of vibrations and thoughts."

Hilario thought for a few moments and concluded:

"Crossing over from the grave effectively imposes peculiar changes on the spirit ... Each traveler on his or her own path, each heart with its own problems."

"Blessed are they who renew themselves for the good!" added Aulus, contentedly. "True love is sublimation in motion through selflessness. Those who cannot yield on behalf of their loved ones' happiness might, of course, love deeply and with caring, but they won't be able to experience the glory of pure love. After death, we usually learn the science of love by sacrificing our dreams so that we may not love according to our own desires, but in conformity with the Lord's Law: mothers obligated to hand their children over to the trials they need; fathers compelled to renew their plans of family protection; wives constrained to entrust their husbands to other sisters; spouses that have to accept second marriages in the home they left behind ... All these are examples of what we find in the vicinity of earth. Death is a call for fraternal understanding ... And when we do not accept its challenge, suffering becomes our lot."

And with a big smile, he added:

"When love does not know how to divide itself, happiness cannot multiply itself."

The conversation continued, interesting and animated, when Abelardo and Celina arrived.

They were comforted and happy.

In the company of his wife, our new friend appeared lighter and more radiant, as if he had absorbed her vitality and joy.

From the look on his face, I could tell that Hilario had a world of questions to ask.

Aulus advised, however:

"Let's go! We need to act quickly."

A short time later, we entered a nebulous region in the darkness of the night.

The stars disappeared from sight.

I got the impression that gasified bitumen was the predominant element in that ambient.

All around us we heard weeping and cursing, but the small lamp that Abelardo now held enabled us to see only the narrow trail that we were supposed to follow.

After a few minutes into our journey, we arrived at a poorly-lit building that housed several patients under the care of attentive care-takers.

We went in.

Aulus explained that we were in one of many emergency hospitals in the purgatorial realms.

Everything spoke of poverty, need and suffering.

"This is my current temple of work," said Abelardo, proud of being an important piece in the apparatus of service there.

We were greeted by brother Justino, the head of the institution.

He apologized for not being able to accompany us. The place was full of discarnate psychopaths, so he couldn't get away for now.

However, he gave us permission to go about freely.

The disharmony was indeed so great that I couldn't hide my astonishment.

How to consider readjustment in such a tormented environment?

The Assistant, however, came to my aid:

"We have to realize that this is a refuge for the desperate. According to the type of reaction they exhibit, they are either taken right away to establishments of positive recovery or they are returned to the areas of affliction whence they came."

We reached the simple bed where a glassy-eyed Liborio showed himself distant to any interest in our presence.

He gazed at us impassively.

He displayed the expression of the mad, transfigured by hidden afflictions.

One of the guards approached us, telling Abelardo that the patient showed increasing anguish.

Aulus examined him paternally and said:

"The thought emitted by the incarnate sister whom Liborio is vampirizing is present in him, tormenting him. They are both attuned to the same wavelength. It's a case of reciprocal persecution. The benefits he received during the meeting are now being eclipsed by suggestions projected from afar."

"So what we have here," I assumed, "is an exact copy of what we commonly see on the earth in the area of tormented mediumship. There are mediums who, relieved of the vexations they endure from lower spirits, quickly call them back, automatically reconnecting with them despite our best efforts to liberate them."

"Yes," Aulus agreed, "as long as their spiritual dispositions are unchanged and until they start thinking differently, they will remain in mutual captivity, where obsessor and obsessed feed on each other's emanations. They fear separation due to the crystallized habits they share according to the principles of affinity, and from there arise the obstacles to the dual recovery that we wish for them."

The patient had become more anxious and paler.

He seemed to be experiencing a dreadful and uncontrollable inner storm.

"Everything points to the proximity of the sister who has seized control of his mind. He shows himself to be even more dominated, more afflicted ..."

Aulus had barely finished his diagnosis when the poor woman, disengaged from her sleeping physical body, appeared, complaining fiercely:

"Liborio! Liborio! Why did you leave? Don't abandon me! Let's go home! Listen to me! Listen!"

"What's this?" asked Hilario intrigued. "Isn't this the same person that the earlier meeting at the center tried to isolate from evil influences?"

Aulus nodded, so Hilario continued:

"Good God! Isn't she interested in recovering her own health? Hasn't she asked for help at the center she attends?"

"That is what she thinks she wants," explained Aulus, carefully. "However, deep down, she feeds on the sickly emanations of her discarnate companion, instinctively holding on to him. There are thousands like her. They display all sorts of infirmities and adapt to them in an accommodation with the least amount of effort. They consider themselves harmed and troubled; however, when their illness is removed and they feel empty and afflicted, they provoke symptoms and impressions with which they evoke the illness to manifest once again but in different ways. This helps them cultivate the position of victims, which pleases them. That happens in most obsession phenomena. Incarnates and discarnates are tied to each other by a strong mutual fascination until the focus of their mental life changes. That is why, on many occasions, greater pains are called to act upon lesser pains, with the purpose of awakening the souls involved in this type of inferior exchange."

By now, the woman had been able to get closer to Liborio, who seemed visibly happy, smiling like a child.

However, when the troubled visitor saw Dona Celina, she started to scream in rage:

"Who's this woman? Tell me! Tell me!"

Our selfless friend approached her humbly and implored:

"My dear sister, calm down! Liborio is exhausted, sick. Let's let him get some rest!"

The woman couldn't stand Celina's gentle and benign demeanor. Far from acknowledging her Spiritist center's kindly medium and blinded with jealousy, she shouted bitter words (not worth repeating) and dashed out of the room.

Liborio was obviously upset, but Aulus applied passes that calmed him down.

Then he told us lovingly:

"As we can see, Divine Goodness is so great that even our less dignified sentiments are used on our behalf. The visitor's spite at finding Celina next to the patient gave us an invaluable reprieve, since we will have a bit of time to help him with some necessary reflections. When she awakens in her physical body tomorrow morning, our poor friend will vaguely remember having dreamed of Liborio in the company of another woman, painting a scene according to her own thinking, for each mind sees in others what it harbors within itself."

Abelardo was satisfied. He caressed the patient, foreseeing his improvement. Hilario pondered, half astonished:

"What amazes me is that, wherever we may be, service never ends: in wakefulness and sleep, in life and in death ..."

Aulus replied with a smile:

"Yes, inertia is simply an illusion, and idleness is an escape that the Law punishes with afflictions from the past."

Our task was now completed so it was time to leave.

Upon saying our goodbyes a few minutes later, Aulus promised to meet us the next evening to continue our observations.

15
Corrupted Abilities

Night was falling...

After the hot day, people were out on the street looking for cooler air.

In keeping with our work plan, we were headed for another Spiritist center with Aulus when loud shouting grabbed our attention.

Two policemen were hauling an elderly man away from a cheap bar. He was deplorably drunk.

The wretch was shouting and cursing in protest.

"Just look at our poor brother!" said Aulus.

And since it wouldn't be long before he was put in the police car, we paused to observe.

Our poor friend was embraced by a spirit of the darkness, as if a strange octopus were absorbing him.

We could see right away that intoxication had gripped both of them because they were completely juxtaposed, displaying the same disturbance.

A few moments later, the car's horn blew hurriedly and our observations were cut short.

"That scene would have offered a valuable lesson..."

In response to Hilario's comment, the Assistant decided that we had enough time to gather a few interesting facts and so he invited us to enter the bar.

It was crowded...

A lot of gaiety, a lot of people.

Inside that place there would certainly be plenty of material for a meaningful lesson.

We entered.

The environment's emanations produced an indefinable sense of discomfort.

Huddled around the inveterate smokers and drinkers were sad, discarnate spirits in a state of longing.

Some of them found happiness and nourishment by inhaling mouthfuls of the smoke blown into the air, still warm from the lungs that had exhaled it. Others were inhaling the breath of impenitent alcoholics.

Nodding toward them, Aulus informed us:

"Many of our brothers and sisters, upon leaving their physical bodies, attach themselves with such delirium to the sensations of the physical experience that they cling to incarnates who are temporarily imbalanced in the unpleasant habits they have surrendered to."

"But why immerse themselves in such a manner in pleasures of this sort?

"Hilario," replied the Assistant kindly, "what life has begun, death will continue ... These individuals had set their minds on the lowest appetites of the world, feeding on emotions that placed them in the vicinity of animality. In spite of having attended places of worship regularly, they were unconcerned with the principles of their faith. They believed that life should be the worship of undignified satisfactions and the victory of the cunning and the strong. The call of death found them in the sphere of dark and criminal postures, and because it is the Law that each soul receives from life in accordance with what it gives, they are interested only in places where they can nurture their particular illusions; in their current situation, they fear the truth and abhor it. They are like the owl that flees the light."

My colleague made a gesture of pity and asked:

"How will they ever change?"

"The day will come when nature itself will empty their cup. There are a thousand processes of readjustment in the Infinite Universe where the Lord's Designs are fulfilled, whether called affliction, disenchantment, fatigue, tedium, suffering, imprisonment..."

"Even so," I pondered, "everything indicates that these unfortunate spirits won't tire of their insane pleasures any time soon."

"I agree completely," replied our instructor, "but in the meantime, the Law can lead them to the regenerative prison."

"How so?"

Hilario's question resonated crystal-clear, and the Assistant explained:

"There are dolorous reincarnations that entail a tremendous expiatory struggle for souls mired in addiction: for instance, Down syndrome, hydrocephalus, paralysis, blindness, secondary epilepsy, severe mental impairment, birth defects and many other anguishing but necessary afflictions that act on behalf of the unbalanced mind from the moment of birth. Most of the time, such curative processes provide good results through the obligatory trials they offer."

"But what if our incarnate brothers and sisters, visibly immersed in dissipation, resolved to reconsider their pathway?" I asked. "What if they returned to regularity through a mental renewal based on the good?"

"Ah! They would gain time, recovering themselves and aiding discarnates ... Using the lever of the will, we can achieve true miracles ... To do so, however, they would have to make a heroic effort."

Observing the drunkards whose glasses were being shared with their invisible partners, Hilario remarked:

"Yesterday, we visited a place where suffering discarnates expressed themselves through individuals in need of assistance, and there we studied something about mediumship ... Here, we are seeing wicked spirits using persons with whom they are attuned in a perfect communion of inferior forces ... Here, as well as at the center, is mediumship at work?"

"Without a doubt," Aulus confirmed. "Psychic resources, at this or that degree of development, are peculiar to everyone, just like locomotion or breathing. They are abilities that the incarnate or discarnate spirit can use either for its benefit or harm. Being a medium doesn't mean that the soul is gifted with privileges or achievements. We often meet persons who are greatly blessed with the gift of mediumship, but who are controlled and subjugated by dark or morally delinquent spirits, with whom they are perfectly attuned, dwelling in scandal and trouble instead of spreading the good. That is why mediumship is not enough for the realization of the work assigned to us. We need the Doctrine of Spiritism, of Pure Christianity, in order to control the mediumistic energy in a way that mobilizes it on behalf of spiritual sublimation in religious faith, just as we control electricity to provide civilization with comfort."

Aulus glanced at some nearby, reserved rooms as if he were familiar with them. Fixing his gaze on a certain door, he invited us to go in.

We followed close behind.

At a table well-provided with fine cognac, a young man was smoking heavily under the control of a spirit whose repulsive appearance was worthy of pity. The man was writing, writing, writing...

"Let's observe," recommended the Assistant.

The young man's brain was drenched in a dark, pasty substance that flowed from the hands of the pitiful brother entwining him.

They were full partners in the authorship of the written material.

The duo didn't notice us.

"In this case," Aulus stated attentively, "our unknown brother is a skilled psychographic medium. His brain cells are fully controlled by the wretched instigator of cruelty under our observation. He is linked to the spirit's imagination and assimilates its ideas, yielding to its dark purposes through the principles of magnetic induction. Because the young man wants to write something dreadful, he has found someone that fortifies his mind and helps him accomplish it."

In a meaningful tone of voice he added:

"We always find what we try to be."

After a brief pause that forced us to reflect, Hilario asked:

"But is he really a medium in the true meaning of the term? Could he take an active part in a common Spiritist group?"

"No. He is not under any spiritualizing discipline. He is a young man with a lively intelligence with little life experience and is controlled by perturbing spirits."

After bending over the two for a few moments, the instructor stated benevolently:

"Amid the excitement of the alcohol and the smoke they are enjoying together, they intend to cause a scandal involving a family going through tough times. A murder has been committed, and at its fringes appears the influence of a certain girl, along with the other multiple causes that triggered the deplorable occurrence. This young man, a friend of an industrious news editor, is himself inclined to malice. With his mental antenna connected to the most unpleasant aspects of the matter, as soon as he agreed to collaborate with his friend, he found the assistance of a tenacious and vicious persecutor of the girl in the spirit world. This spirit wants to exaggerate her participation in the murder in order to beat down her apprehensive mind and make her fall into the abuses of youth..."

"But how?" asked an alarmed Hilario.

"Once in possession of the libelous article, the editor will be the vehicle of harmful information to the public. The girl, from one moment to the next, will be exposed to the most heartless accusations and will certainly become very troubled since she did not play a role in the crime the way they intend to report it. The obsessor, calculatedly using the young man with whom he is attuned, means for the piece to cause a sensation. He wants to disparage her moral life and thus break her character, dragging her down, if possible, to the vicious swamp where he dwells."

"Will he be successful?" insisted my colleague, astonished.

"Who knows?"

And somewhat sad, Aulus added:

"Naturally, the girl must have chosen the type of trials she is undergoing, willing to struggle valiantly against temptations."

"But what if she can't fight with the strength required?"

"It would be better to say, 'if she doesn't want to,' for the Law does not entrust us with problems that exceed our ability to resolve. Thus, if she decides not to fight against the destructive influence, she will dwell for a long time in such afflictions because, in principle, she is already tied to them."

"And all because?..."

Hilario's question hung in the air as a troubled interrogation, but Aulus eased our minds:

"Undoubtedly, the young woman and the wretch persecuting her have been linked to each other for a long, long time ... They must have been together in the lower realms of the spirit world prior to the girl's present beneficial reincarnation. Encountering her again in the physical experience – whose advantages he does not yet share – her unfortunate companion is trying once more to imbalance her emotionally in order to exploit her in a vampirizing action."

Aulus paused briefly, smiled sorrowfully and added:

"However, to speak of the matter would mean opening the gripping pages of a large novel, and that would lead us away from our objective. Let's stick to mediumship."

In an attempt to lead the conversation away from the numerous questions whirling in Hilario's head, I pondered:

"This scene should induce us to meditate on the general phenomena of interaction with the spirit world, which happens to all humankind without its perception."

"Right!" agreed the Assistant. "Mediumistic faculties and collaboration from the spirit world are everywhere. Wherever there is thought, there are mental currents, and wherever there are mental currents, there is association. And every association entails interdependence and mutual influence. So we can see how necessary it is to live nobly so that we can attract thoughts that ennoble us. Dignified work, goodness, fraternal understanding, serving our fellow beings, respect for nature, and prayer are the best means of assimilating the higher principles of life. In the realm of ideas, we give and receive in spirit according to universal laws that we cannot deceive."

With a silent gesture reminding us of our duties, the Assistant invited us to leave.

We went back out onto the street.

We had barely taken a step when an ambulance went by slowly with its siren blaring to clear the way.

In the seat beside the driver sat a man with gray hair framing his pleasant but worried face. Next to him, however, embracing him tenderly and naturally, a spirit in a lily white garment enveloped his head in soft, calming radiations of silvery light.

"Oh!" Hilario asked curious, "who's that man in such fine company?"

Aulus smiled and explained:

"Not everything on the common path is corrupted energy. That is probably a physician on some life-saving endeavor."

"But is he a Spiritist?"

"With all the respect we owe Spiritism, it is imperative to remember that the Lord's Blessing can descend on any religious expression. Above all, the man is most likely a humanitarian and benevolent professional, who, because of his habit of aiding his neighbor, now merits the assistance he is receiving. It would not be enough to be a Spiritist or a doctor to retain the beneficent influence that accompanies him. To accommodate himself so harmoniously with such a spirit, he must have a clear conscience and a heart that radiates peace and fraternity."

"But can we classify him as a medium?" asked my companion, somewhat disappointed.

"And why not? He's a medium of blessed human values, especially in assisting the sick, where he channels the mental currents of spirits of the good, devoted to loving the sufferers of the world."

With an expressive inflection in his voice, he added:

"As we can see, the influences of good or evil in this evolutionary sphere extend everywhere, and everywhere we can register the presence of mediumistic faculties that assimilate such influences according to the happy or unhappy, correct or unworthy way in which each mind places itself. Thus, by studying mediumship in Spiritist sanctuaries faithful to Jesus, we observe a power peculiar to all individuals, of general benefit if under a guidance capable of disciplining and leading it to the utmost service in the good. Take electricity, for example, which little by little is transforming the face of the world. It is not enough to have a powerful waterfall with the potential of millions of horsepower. A power plant has to be built next to it to control its resources, intelligently setting them in motion and distributing them according to everyone's needs ... Otherwise, the waterfall will continue to be a living picture of phenomenal beauty, but an irretrievable waste."

Time did not allow us to continue our conversation, so we headed for a group where our studies of the previous evening would resume.

16
The Mediumistic Mandate

It was almost 8:00 p.m. when we stopped in front of an austere-looking building surrounded by several vehicles.

A lot of people were coming and going.

A large number of discarnates were gathered both inside and outside the structure.

Guards from our plane flanked the building, attentively preventing the entry of impenitent or mocking spirits.

Various groups of people went inside, but once in the lobby they were separated from certain spirits that were accompanying them. These spirits were not merely curious or suffering, but blasphemers and obstinate in evil.

These cases were an exception, however, because most of the group of discarnate brothers and sisters was composed of afflicted and sick spirits in as much need of fraternal help as the ill and distressed patients they were accompanying.

We went in.

A large table in the center of the spacious room was surrounded by a large, luminous, insulating band.

A large area was reserved around the table to accommodate those in need of assistance, whether incarnate or not. This area, too, was protected by bands of magnetic defense under the watchful care of guards from our sphere of action.

In front of and opposite the entrance, several spirit benefactors were conferring with one another, and nearby, a respectable-looking woman was listening attentively to various patients.

The woman was enveloped in a broad aura of opalescent light, and in spite of the projections of dark substances directed at her through the requisitions of the sufferers she was assisting, her aura remained unaffected, with the noxious fluids unable to penetrate it.

The Assistant informed us:

"That is our sister Ambrosina, who for over 20 years has sought to offer her best to Christian mediumship. Out of love for our ideals, she has renounced the simplest joys of the world, including the broader comforts of a home. Ever since her younger years, she has been working without the solace of marriage.

Ambrosina's face looked frail and wrinkled, but it reflected the peace that vibrated within her.

On her head, amid her graying hair, a small cone of light rested like a delicate adornment.

Intrigued, we asked Aulus about it and he explained without hesitation:

"That is an ultra sensitive magnetic device through which the medium is in constant contact with the spirit responsible for the spiritual work she is doing. Because of the time she has dedicated to the Cause of the Good and because of her many sacrifices, Ambrosina received a mediumistic service mandate from the Higher Spheres, thereby meriting the responsibility of a closer association with the instructor who presides over her tasks. She has become so well-known that she is overwhelmed by all sorts of requests. By inspiring hope and faith in all who approach her ministry of fraternity and understanding, she is naturally beset by the most disconcerting pleas."

"So, she is overburdened by petitions and requests?" asked Hilario, unavoidably curious.

"To a certain point, yes, since she symbolizes a bridge between two worlds. However, with evangelical patience, she knows how to help others help themselves because it would be impossible for her to solve all the problems she is confronted with."

We approached the respectable and modest medium, and we could see that she was pensive, in spite of the loud voices around her.

Nearby, the combined thoughts of two persons exteriorized the lamentable scenes of a crime they had committed.

Dona Ambrosina tuned in to them in thought and spoke without words in sentences that only we could hear: "Dear spirit friends, what to do? I am aware of our delinquent brothers' crime ... A man was murdered ... I can see his agony portrayed in their memories ... What are these fugitives of earthly justice looking for in our midst?"

We could see that the medium was fearful of losing her vibratory harmony.

She didn't want to be absorbed by any worries about the two visitors.

One of the mentors present approached and set her at ease:

"Ambrosina, don't fear. Be calm. We must not let affliction trouble us. You must see our unfortunate brothers as creatures worthy of pity. Remember that we are here to assist, and that the remedy was not created for the healthy. Be compassionate, sustaining your own balance! We are debtors of love and respect towards one another and the greater our misfortune, the greater the assistance we need. We must welcome our brothers compromised by evil as patients in need of our care."

The medium settled down.

She began conversing naturally with the frequenters of the place.

Here, someone wanted help for a tormented heart or for help on behalf of unfortunate family members; there, pleas for fraternal aid on behalf of patients in despair; yonder, other assistance requests.

Dona Ambrosina would console and promise help, stating that once Gabriel, her spirit guide arrived, the matter would be presented to him. Certainly, he would know how to proceed.

A few moments later, Gabriel, the lead mentor of the center, entered the room followed by a large group of friends.

Conversing warmly, they gathered at the table. There, these spirits of a nobler mental life naturally established a broad band of light that was inaccessible to the darkness that enveloped most of the incarnates and discarnates at the large gathering.

Gabriel and his assistants greeted us benevolently.

It seemed that we were taking part in a dazzling festivity, such was the joy of the spirit instructors and spirit workers of that institution. Caring for the sick and the suffering of the two realms did not rob them of their hope, peace, and optimism. Accompanying the selfless and enlightened Gabriel – who merited Aulus's highest demonstrations of respect – were discarnate doctors, teachers, nurses and auxiliaries ready to serve in the harvest field of the good.

They radiated such beauty and joy that Hilario, as dazzled as I was, returned to the questions that characterized his youthful temperament.

Considering the messages of light and sympathy they were projecting might they be high ambassadors of Divine Providence? Did they perchance live among the saints? Might they be in personal communion with Christ himself? Had they reached the condition of sinless beings?"

The Assistant smiled good-humoredly and explained:

"None of that. Despite all the esteem we owe them, we have to see them as vanguards of progress; but they are not infallible. They are noble souls in the blessed process of sublimation, creditors of our reverence due to the degree of spiritual advancement they have reached. However, they are spirits still attached to earthly humanity, amongst whom they will assume physical bodies once again in the future through the universal institution of reincarnation to carry out invaluable endeavors."

"But when compared with this assembly of tormented souls, are they luminaries exempt of error?"

"No. We cannot expect them to have qualities possessed only by spirits who have reached absolute sublimation. They are high-ranking exponents of fraternity and higher knowledge, but they still harbor the natural potential to err. They excel in goodwill, learning and personal sacrifice in their incessant assistance to incarnates, but they can still fall victim to errors. Even so, they are quick to correct them without the vanity that often afflicts the learned people of earth. For instance, there are several discarnate physicians among them. In spite of being excellent professionals dedicated to the mission they have embraced, it would not be admissible that they would suddenly be promoted from the fragmentary medical knowledge of the world to complete wisdom. With their immersion in the realities of death, they have acquired new visions of life, expanding their horizons of observation. They understand that they do know something, but it is very little of what they ought to know. Consequently, they are devoting themselves to invaluable crusades of service in which they help and learn. Workers from other circles of human experience are in a similar situation – they help and are helped in turn. It could not be otherwise. We know that miracles do not exist as a derogation of the laws of nature. We are one another's brothers and sisters, evolving together in a process of interdependence where individual effort stands out."

At this point of his explanation, Dona Ambrosina sat down beside the director of the session, a pleasant-looking gray-haired man who had set up the worktable for fourteen persons. He displayed simplicity and faith.

While Gabriel stood beside the medium, applying longitudinal passes to prepare her for the evening's activities, the leader of the meeting said a heartfelt prayer.

Next, an edifying text from a doctrinal book was read, followed by a brief evangelical message chosen by the meeting's director under Gabriel's influence.

The main theme of the reading was patience.

And truly, the assembly examined in its entirety displayed the afflictions of disquieting problems, demanding the key of conformance to reach re-equilibrium.

Dozens of people crowded around the table, exhibiting tribulations and difficulties.

Strange thought-forms emerged from group to group, evidencing their mental positions.

Here, darts of concern, daggers of bitterness, mists of tears ... There, obsessors hardened in disappointment or despair amid aggressive purposes of vengeance, worsened by the fear of the unknown...

Many of the discarnates longed for heaven, while others feared hell, maladjusted by the mistaken religious education they had received.

Several spirit friends began helping the mediums presiding at the table to expand on the doctrinal message based on the evangelical topic of the evening by providing rightful comments, encouragement and consolation.

Cases were not addressed individually, although we clearly perceived that the messages were emitted with precise aims: here, they uplifted a broken heart; there, they warned careless consciences; yonder, they renewed forgiveness, faith, charity and hope.

There was no lack of gripping scenes of persecuting spirits trying to hypnotize their victims, inducing them to sleep so that they wouldn't hear the transforming messages.

Although several other mediums were at work in the room, collaborating for the harmony of the services in general, we could see that Dona Ambrosina was the center of everyone's trust and the object of their attention.

She was the heart of the sanctuary, giving and receiving, the living focus of the silent connection between the inhabitants of two distinct spheres.

Several sheets of paper were placed next to her as she prayed.

These were petitions, wishes and appeals from the attendees, seeking help from the Other Side with their afflictions and difficulties.

Each sheet was an agonized petition, a moving plea.

A wide elastic band of bluish light could be seen between Dona Ambrosina and Gabriel, and spirit friends, ready in Christian solidarity, entered it. One by one they took the medium's arm – after influencing her cortical centers – to respond as far as possible to the problems.

Prior to beginning the task of responding to the questions, however, the spirit workers placed a large, fluidic mirror next to the medium. On its face, with incredible rapidity, absent persons named in the petitions would appear in order to be examined by the benefactors, who from a distance would contemplate the image, pick up its thoughts, specify its needs and offer a possible solution.

While other knowledgeable workers of faith were teaching the path to inner peace under the inspiration of mentors from our plane, Dona Ambrosina tirelessly psychographed under the guidance of instructors who took turns in the assistance task.

The work in the room had assumed a steady pace, which gave us the appropriate window to continue our questions.

Hilario was the first to ask about something we could not grasp. Glancing at the wide fluidic band that linked Dona Ambrosina to Gabriel, he asked:

"What's the purpose of that band, in which the medium and the mentor are so closely associated to one another?"

With his usual tolerance and benevolence, Aulus explained:

"The greater development of mediumistic faculties requires this measure. While listening and seeing within vibrations that transcend the ordinary sensorial field, Ambrosina cannot be left at the mercy of every request from the spirit realm or she would lose her equilibrium. When through goodwill, study and comprehension of their responsibilities, mediums show they are ready to work for the good, they receive closer support from an experienced and knowledgeable spirit who begins guiding their pilgrimage on earth and controlling their energies. In this case, Gabriel fully controls the energies of Ambrosina, who establishes contact with the spirit realm solely in conformance with his supervision."

"Does that mean that in order to establish a communication through her, we would have to tune in to both her and Gabriel at the same time?"

"Exactly. A mediumistic mandate requires order, security and efficiency. A delegation of human authority involves concession of resources on the part of those who grant it. One cannot request regular cooperation from mediums without offering them the necessary guarantees."

"But doesn't that make the process of communication difficult?"

"Not at all. In light of respectable and understandable needs showing prospects for real improvement, Gabriel has taken it upon himself to facilitate matters, helping the communicators as much as he aids the medium."

Noticing the perfect communion between mentor and ward, I asked in turn if such an association might not be connected to commitments assumed by mediums prior to reincarnation.

"Oh yes! Such work is not carried out without prior planning. Chance is a word of human invention to disguise least effort. Gabriel and Ambrosina planned their current work long before she enveloped herself in the dense fluids of physical life."

"So why say," I continued, remembering the Assistant's own words, "'that when mediums distinguish themselves in their service to the good they receive the support of a spirit friend,' if that spirit friend and the medium have been united for a long time?"

The Instructor replied:

"In any commitment, it would not be right to lessen freedom of action. Ambrosina did commit herself, but that wouldn't keep her from backing out of her agreement, despite recognizing its excellence and magnitude. She could have followed another pathway to fulfill her dreams as a woman, even if it would have delayed the accomplishments without which she will not freely lift herself from the world. The Guides of the spirit world seek collaborators, not slaves. The medium worthy of the mission of assistance is not a yoked animal, but a brother or sister of humankind and an aspirant of Wisdom. Mediums should work and study out of love ... That's why many start the journey and then retreat. Free to decide their own destiny, they often prefer to stagnate in the circle of undesirable company, yielding to terrible fascinations. They start out enthusiastically in the work of the good, but in many circumstances they heed the corrupt spirits that approach them when they let their guard down. Consequently, they stumble and give in to cupidity, idleness, destructive self-centeredness or delinquent sexuality and become puppets of the enemies of the light, who vampirize their energies and destroy their greatest potential. This has been the case down through time."

"Yes, yes," I agreed, "but wouldn't it be possible for the spirit mentors take measures to put a stop to such abuses the moment they appear?"

Aulus smiled and replied respectfully:

"Each conscience progresses by its own volition, in spite of the many teachers on the path. We owe our defeat or victory to ourselves. Souls and collectivities acquire the experiences with which they redeem or elevate themselves through their own efforts. Human beings construct, destroy and reconstruct destinies, just as humankind builds and destroys civilizations, seeking the best direction to respond to God's call. That is why heavy tribulations roam the world – infirmity and affliction, war and decadence – awakening souls to rightful discernment. Each person lives in the sphere of his or her own acquisitions or debts. Thus, we see millions of individuals on earth caught in the web of tormented mediumship, thousands possessing noteworthy psychic potential, many trying to develop resources of such nature, but few obtaining a mediumistic mandate for the work of fraternity and light. And as we are now, sublimated mediumship is a service we must edify, even though this glorious acquisition may cost us many centuries."

"But even with a mediumistic mandate, could someone like Dona Ambrosina actually fail?"

"Why not?" stressed the Assistant. "A mandate is a delegation of power obtained through moral credit, but it isn't a certificate of sanctification. With greater or lesser responsibilities, we mustn't forget our obligations concerning the Divine law in order to consolidate our titles of worthiness in the life eternal."

And with a meaningful tone of voice, Aulus added:

"Let us recall the words of the Lord: *Much will be asked of those who have received much.*"

The conversation, in addition to the tasks performed at the meeting, had offered me plenty of material to think about.

The Assistant's invaluable remarks regarding mediumship compelled me to silence and reflection.

The same was not true of my companion, however. Hilario was gazing at the fluidic mirror on which the benefactors from our plane gathered quick information for the questions posed, and asked Aulus for some clarification on the delicate, efficient device, which, from time to time, displayed scenes with distressed or sickly persons.

"It's a type of television endowed with resources from our sphere."

"Does the mirror display the physical body or the soul itself?" asked Hilario, looking for particulars.

"The soul itself. By examining the perispirit, information and conclusions are lined up. Often, it's crucial to meticulously analyze certain cases presented to us; however, when we receive multiple appeals all at the same time, we utilize means to tend to them at distance. To do so, workers in our line of activity are sent to diverse regions, where they capture the images according to the requests addressed to us, synchronizing the emissions with this receiver. The television, which has begun to spread throughout the world[12], can offer a close idea of this service, although our transmissions are much simpler, exact and instantaneous."

My colleague thought for a few moments as if a serious problem had blossomed in his mind, and then asked:

"What we are seeing suggests important considerations. Let's say that someone addresses a question to the mediumistic mandate that would entail a certain delay between request and response ... Let's also say that the interested party who is far away discarnates, and, as occurs on many occasions, remains as a spirit in a home or hospital bed although already free of the physical body ... In such a case, is the spirit benefactor's reply given as if it applied to the person while incarnate?"

"That can happen in various circumstances," added the Assistant, "because our line of service is neither automatic nor miraculous. We act with a spirit of cooperation and goodwill; the success depends on our mutual assistance because one single part can't fix the problems of the entire machine. The workers that receive the information require the efficient concourse of those who transmit it. Many times, the sufferer is shown from a long distance to those who propose to help him or her, and because of the normally huge number of the afflicted they must assist, the Samaritans of fraternity cannot immediately tell if they are receiving information about an incarnate or discarnate, especially if they haven't had a large amount of experience. In certain situations, those in need require intensive assistance in a fraction of a minute. Thus, any inaccuracy of this kind is perfectly admissible."

"But wouldn't that disturb the service of faith?" asked Hilario. "If we were the incarnates, wouldn't we see this as a useless response sent to a *dead person*?"

---

[12] This book was written in the 1950s. – Tr.

"No, Hilario, we cannot state the issue in such terms. Those who sincerely seek faith find the reward of the clear and peaceful comprehension of things without any harm due to superficial and apparent contradictions."

The Assistant thought for a moment and remarked:

"But if the patients are examples of frivolousness and bad faith, approaching the mediumistic work with the deliberate purpose of instigating disbelief and spiritual aridity, the results, when they do occur, will serve them as a just harvest for the thorns they have sown. They abuse the generosity and patience of spirit friends and end up harvesting denial and mental torment for themselves. Those who cast mud into a clean fountain cannot expect to draw pure water from it right afterward."

Hilario was satisfied and became silent.

While Dona Ambrosina and the others were fulfilling their edifying duties, two healing mediums started the service of magnetic passes to treat sick patients in a nearby room. In order to gather new knowledge, we turned our attention to them.

17
The Service of Passes

We crossed the door and were greeted by a soothing and luminous ambient.

Flanked by spirits obviously connected with the service of healing, an elderly gentleman and a distinguished lady were making notes in a small notebook.

Indicating the two mediums, the Assistant informed us:

"These are Clara and Henrique. They provide assistance under the guidance of spirit friends."

"What about the radiance of the atmosphere?" ventured Hilario curiously.

"This room," explained Aulus kindly, "is filled with the sublimated mental emanations of the majority of those who seek magnetic assistance with love and trust. It is a sort of 'inner altar', created by the thoughts, prayers and aspirations of those who approach us with their best intentions."

We didn't have time, however, for a long conversation.

Clara and Henrique, now in prayer, became surrounded by an aura of light.

They looked as if they were almost disengaged from their physical bodies, showing themselves spiritually freer and in full contact with the benefactors present, although not able to see them.

Calm and self-assured, they seemed to be absorbing reinvigorating energies within their souls. They understood that prayer kept their spirits in communication with an invisible and profound source of silent energy.

On the other side of the closed door, afflicted and rowdy people jostled each other, waiting for the preparations to finish.

The two mediums, however, appeared to be spiritually far-away.

Enveloped by the group of fraternal spirits, they registered their instructions through intuitive recourses.

Judging from the radiations from Henrique's magnetic personality, it was immediately apparent that he was more spiritually evolved than his companion. Of the two, he was the leading figure.

Obviously because of this, standing next to him was the spirit guide that was better fit for the task.

Aulus greeted him and introduced us.

Our new acquaintance, brother Conrado, embraced us warmly, telling us that we could take all the notes we wanted to during the task about to start.

Aulus, on his part, said we could ask Conrado any questions that might come up.

Hilario, who never held his spontaneity in check, respectfully began his usual questioning:

"Do you come here often?"

"Yes, two nights a week we are responsible for the center's work on behalf of the sick."

"Are the patients incarnates only?"

"Not at all. We take care of the needy of whatever nature."

"Do you have a lot of helpers?"

"We are a team of helpers, according to the structure established by mentors in the Higher Realms."

"Do you mean that in a Spiritist center, such as this one, there are spirit collaborators enrolled as doctors and nurses, just like in an ordinary hospital on earth?"

"Exactly. Amongst incarnates, as well as amongst those of us who are still a long ways from spiritual perfection, the success of our work demands experience, punctuality, security and responsibility from the faithful worker. The Law cannot disparage the lines of logic."

"And the mediums? Are they always the same ones?"

"Yes, but if they have an excusable absence they can be replaced, although in such situations the work inevitably suffers some small hindrances resulting from the natural lack of adjustment."

My colleague directed an uncertain glance at the two mediums in prayer and continued:

"Do they always prepare themselves through prayer before the work starts?"

"Of course. Prayer is a prodigious pouring out of energies due to the vigorous mental current it attracts. Through prayer, Clara and Henrique expel from their inner worlds the gloomy remnants from their daily circle of struggle and they absorb from our plane the renewing substances they replenish themselves with in order to work effectively on behalf of their neighbor. Thus, they offer help and end up being helped in turn."

"That means they don't have to worry about getting exhausted ..."

"Indeed. Like us, they do not come here with the intension of being grantors of benefits, but as beneficiaries who receive in order to give. Prayer, along with the acknowledgement of our unworthiness, makes us humble links in a chain of assistance whose guidance resides in the Higher Spheres. Those of us in this room who are consecrated to the evangelical mission under Jesus' inspiration are somewhat like an electric outlet, allowing the flow of a force that is not our own and which serves in the production of energy and light."

The explanations couldn't have been clearer.

And while Hilario smiled, satisfied, Conrado tapped Henrique's shoulders as if to remind him of the work schedule. Although he hadn't registered the gesture through a physical sensation, the medium immediately obeyed, walking over to the door and opening it to the sufferers.

A small crowd of incarnates and discarnates congregated at the entrance, their movements controlled by personnel of the center.

Conrado turned to the task at hand and we rejoined the Assistant.

Both mediums got to work.

Patients of all kinds entered with great hope, and after being attended to, left with obvious signs of comfort. Luminous sparks radiated from Clara's and Henrique's hands, supplying them with vigor and renewed strength.

In most cases, they didn't have to touch the patients' body directly. Magnetic resources applied at close range penetrated their "vital halo" or aura, causing sudden changes.

The pass-givers were like two human batteries, emitting rays of multiple kinds that flowed from their hands after passing through their own heads upon contact with brother Conrado and his collaborators.

The sight was truly fascinating due to the plays of light.

After probing the scene, Hilario asked Aulus:

"Why does the energy transmitted by our spirit friends pass first through the mediums' heads?"

"Even here," said Aulus, "we cannot underestimate the importance of the mind. Thought plays a decisive role in the giving of healing principles. Unless the medium's mind is illuminated by faith and good will, he or she will not connect with the spirits who work upon these foundations."

"However," I pondered, "there are persons well endowed with magnetic energy but completely unconcerned with the moral aspect!"

"Yes," agreed the Assistant. "You are referring to common hypnotizers who are often bearers of exceptional energy. Their demonstrations are beautiful, impressive and convincing, but they work in the sphere of pure phenomena without any edifying purposes in the area of spirituality. We mustn't forget, Andre, that magnetic potential is common to all individuals, although it is expressed in an infinite number of ways."

"Yet such professionals can also heal!" pointed out my companion, completing my remarks.

"Yes, they can heal, but accidentally, when the patient deserves immediate spiritual assistance, as well as the intervention of friends that are willing to help. However, those who abuse this fountain of energy by exploiting it for their personal gain almost always debase themselves. They don't know what they're messing with, and guided solely by vanity or ambition, they inevitably encounter spirits with whom they are attuned and wind up falling into difficult situations that we'll not go into for now. If they are not of a lofty character that can act as a barrier to corrupting influences, they end up vampirized by energies stronger than theirs. If we look at the matter only from the point of view of capacity, we are compelled to realize that there is a huge number of powerful spiritual hypnotizers in the tormented circles of ignorance and cruelty, the origin of the most afflictive cases of obsession."

And smiling, he added:

"Look at nature. The snake is one of the greatest holders of hypnotic power."

"Then to heal," said Hilario, "certain behavior on the part of the spirit is indispensable."

"Unquestionably. A noble heart and a pure mind are indispensable in the exercise of love, humility and living faith so that the rays of the divine power may find access and flow through us for the benefit of others. This is crucial for an ongoing service of healing."

"But for an endeavor of such nature, do we need to choose people who are obligated to carry out special studies?"

"We have to consider the fact that in any line of work a lack of study means stagnation. This or that coworker who gives up learning and incorporating new knowledge inevitably condemns him or herself to a lower line of work; however, in the case of magnetic assistance, such as the kind offered here, we need to keep in mind that the task is one of pure solidarity with an ardent desire to help under the invocation of prayer. Every prayer – the child of sincerity and a duty well-filled with moral respectability and clean sentiments – is imbued with incommensurable power. With the matter analyzed in such terms, any worthy and devoted person can use prayer to win the sympathy of the venerable magnetizers on the Spirit Plane, who then mobilize them to spread the good. We aren't talking about showy hypnotism, but a place of healing, where mediums transmit the benefits they receive without the pretense that they themselves are the originators. We mustn't forget this truth to be very clear that wherever there is humility and love, divine assistance is sure and immediate."

The healing ministry was proceeding effectively and peacefully, demanding our attention.

The patients entered two at a time and were lovingly received by Clara and Henrique under the providential assistance of Conrado and his collaborators.

Obsessed persons came in accompanied by their cold-hearted tormentors; at the mediums' touch on the cortical region, they immediately withdrew. Nonetheless, they remained in the vicinity, waiting for their victims, most of whom they reunited with right away.

In surmising the situation, we saw that some of the patients didn't improve at all.

The magnetic radiations couldn't penetrate their organic vessels.

This phenomenon prompted Hilario to ask why.

"They lack faith," explained the Assistant.

"So, faith is essential for them to register the assistance they need?"

"Yes, indeed! In photography we need the photographic plate to hold the image, and with electricity we need a wire that can conduct the current. Regarding spiritual assistance, it is essential that the patient display a certain "favorable tension." This tension derives from faith. Of course, we are not referring to religious fanaticism or blind ignorance, but the attitude of inner assurance, with reverence and submission to the Divine Laws, in whose wisdom and love we seek support. Without introspection and respect, we cannot fixate the imponderable resources that work on our behalf, because scorn and hardness of heart can be compared to thick layers of ice on the temple of the soul."

The lesson was simple and beautiful.

Hilario became quiet, perhaps to reflect on it in silence.

Attentive to the objectives of our study, Aulus considered the expediency of our direct contact with the work at hand. We could benefit from examining a few of the cases in question.

To that end, he approached an elderly woman who had just entered seeking help, and with Conrado's permission, he asked us to examine her as carefully as possible.

While awaiting Clara's help, the woman had difficulty standing up with her large abdomen. She was grimacing in pain.

"Look at her liver!"

Utilizing the resources within our reach, we began examining it.

Sure enough, the organ was dilated: a characteristic of people suffering from heart failure. The hepatic cells looked like a large beehive working under enormous stress. The congested gallbladder led me to immediately inspect the intestines. The bile, under compression, had reached the vessels and was compromising the blood. The blocked bile duct made the diagnosis easy. A cursory examination of the ocular conjunctiva confirmed my impression.

The jaundice was obvious.

After listening to my diagnosis, Conrado confirmed:

"Yes, it's a case of complex jaundice. It was caused by a terrible fit of rage that our friend threw at home. Perturbed and giving in to exasperation, she developed an obstinate hepatitis, which resulted in the jaundice."

"How can she be helped?"

Conrado placed his hand on the medium's forehead and sent her a radiant current of energy that inspired her to move her hands over the patient from her head down to the diseased liver.

We noticed that the encephalic cortex was covered with a luminous substance that descended in very fine threads to reach the visceral area.

The woman displayed an unmistakable expression of relief on her face. She left, visibly happy, promising that she would return to continue the treatment.

Hilario looked questioningly at the Assistant and asked:

"Is our sister healed?"

"Impossible," said Aulus paternally. "She has organs and vessels that have been damaged; it will take a long time for here to heal."

"What will her healing entail?"

"Passes are a transfusion of energies that alter the cellular field. You know that nowadays, even in human science, the atom is no longer the indivisible building block of matter; that behind it, there are lines of force agglutinating the subatomic principles; and that behind these principles lies the determining mental life ... Everything derives from the mind in the sanctuary of nature. If we would renew our thoughts, everything would change for us. In magnetic assistance, emission and reception are entwined, helping needy patients so that they can help themselves. The re-energized mind revitalizes the microscopic lives that serve it in the temple of the body, erecting valuable reconstructions. As we can see, passes are an important contribution for those who know how to receive them with the respect and trust that they entail."

"Can passes be given at a distance?"

"Yes, as long as there is attunement between the one who administers them and the one who receives them. In such a case, several spirits cooperate to perform this type of assistance, and prayer is the best vehicle for the healing energy."

The work around us continued intensely.

Aulus thought that our presence might overload Conrado's concerns and that it wouldn't be appropriate for us to remain much longer; after all, we had obtained the brief information we had wanted. In light of this, we bade farewell to the supervisor and returned to the main room in order to continue our blessed learning experience.

18
Side Notes

Dona Ambrosina continued to psychograph several messages addressed to the attendees.

One of the speakers, under the influence of a benign spirit benefactor, was emphasizing the need to conform to the Divine Laws in order to restructure our mental life, thereby meriting renewing blessings.

Some of the incarnates remained lethargic and impermeable, vampirized by the capricious obsessing spirits that followed them closely. However, several discarnates of average understanding were listening attentively and sincerely to the consoling teaching.

Gabriel presided firmly over everything with his lucid and penetrating eyes.

Nothing, no matter how small, escaped his perception.

Here, at his slightest gesture, mocking spirits were encouraged to renew their attitude; there, sick patients were aided after his silent nod of recommendation.

His strong and sure pulse of command upheld the harmony and order of the whole endeavor.

We contemplated the large table where supervision unfolded with irreprehensible equilibrium. Observing the busy medium surrounded by what she needed for her work, Hilario asked Aulus:

"Why are there so many personal messages from the kind spirits?"

"They are comforting responses for those who ask for their assistance and consolation."

"And these responses, do they offer cut-and-dried solutions to their problems?"

"No. There's always a gap between help and solution in any difficulty, and we mustn't forget that each one of us has his or her own enigmas."

"If that's the case, why the communications? If discarnates cannot offer a peaceable conclusion to the torments of their incarnate brothers and sisters, why is the door open between them and us?"

"Don't forget the need for cooperation on each person's pathway," replied Aulus gravely. "As far as eternal life is concerned, life in the physical body, no matter how long, is always a short learning experience. And we must also bear in mind that the earth is the arena where we wage our evolutionary battle. Amid the principles of cause and effect, we acquire the qualities of experience, with which we structure our personality for the Higher Realms. Actually, the mind is the traveler seeking the goal of the angelic state, but it cannot proceed without help. No one lives alone. The so-called dead must help incarnate brothers and sisters during their stage in dense matter because they themselves will in turn be compelled to new immersions in the corporeal experience. It is the Law that wisdom rescues ignorance, and that the more evolved aid those who are less so. By cooperating with enlightened and benevolent spirits. incarnates attract invaluable help for their lives in the spirit world, and the spirit friends who assist incarnates are building resources for tomorrow, when they will return to the terrestrial struggle."

"Yes, yes, I see," said Hilario gratefully. "However, putting myself in the position of normal people, I recall that, in the world, we normally hope for a decisive and absolute solution from heaven to solve our innumerable problems."

"That attitude," emphasized the Assistant, "derives from an old mental vice. To understand the matter better, let's remember the Divine Master's exemplary life. Jesus, the Spiritual Governor of the World, aided the sick and the afflicted without exempting them from their fundamental problems. Zacchaeus, the wealthy man blessed by the Master's visit, felt constrained to change his conduct. Mary Magdalene, who received the Master's loving consideration, was not freed from the arduous battle for inner renewal. Lazarus, raised from the darkness of the tomb, was not exonerated from having to accept the challenge of death later on. Paul of Tarsus was singled out by a personal appeal at the gates of Damascus, yet the apostle did not get a dispensation from the sacrifices inherent to his new mission. As we know, it would be illogical to expect discarnates to be free from all human struggles. That would imply stealing the work that sustains the worker or withholding the lesson from the student in need of enlightenment."

Nearby, a kindly woman was thinking to herself:

"My son! My son! If you're not dead, please visit me! Come! Come! I'm dying from missing you! ... Say something that both of us can understand ... If all is not over, approach the medium and communicate! It's impossible that you could have no pity."

Her bitter words, although unarticulated, reached our ears as if flung into the air in a muted voice.

A slight noise behind us got our attention.

A discarnate young man appeared in a deplorable condition and approached the brokenhearted woman, dominated by an invincible attraction.

From his curled lips poured all his anguish in the form of emotional words:

"Mother! Mother!" he cried out on his knees like a tormented child, leaning into her lap. "Please, don't forsake me! ... I'm here; listen to me! I'm not dead! ... Forgive me! Forgive me! ... I'm a rebel, a castaway! ... I sought death when I should have lived for your love! I now know firsthand what suffering is and I wish I could die for good, so great is the shame that afflicts my heart!"

Of course the poor woman couldn't see the agonized figure, but she felt his presence through an indescribable anxiety oppressing her chest.

Two caretakers approached and took the young man from his mother's lap. Following the Assistant as he rushed to help the tearful woman, we heard her clamor mentally:

"Wouldn't it be better to follow him?! To die and rest! ... My son; I want my son!"

Aulus applied magnetic passes, after which the poor woman felt great relief. Then, he told us:

"Let's review the case of this poor misguided mother. Her son committed suicide a few months ago and she hasn't been able to calm her inner torment. In her loving devotion, she pleads for him to communicate. But she doesn't realize what she's asking for because the young man's shocking situation would cause her dreadful suffering. For that reason, she cannot receive his words directly. However, by being in contact with the spiritual work carried out here, she will acquire new energies to gradually recover."

"Of course," added Hilario intelligently, "she will not have resolved the problem of her wounded sentiments, but she will acquire enough strength to get better."

"That's right."

"Moreover," I considered in turn, "mediumship nowadays is essentially the same as prophecy in the religions of the past."

"Yes," agreed Aulus attentively, "with the difference that mediumship nowadays is a gift from the Lord to humankind in general, considering the maturity of humankind's understanding of life. The mediumistic phenomenon is not new. Only the way it manifests is new because the priesthood of various creeds has been stagnated for many centuries in the displays of outward worship, unduly mummifying the body of the heavenly revelations. Most notably, Christianity, which should be the largest and simplest of the schools of faith, has long been crystallized in the superficiality of its churches. Thus, it was necessary to free its principles for the benefit of the world, which nowadays, from a scientific point of view, is bathed in the light of a new era. That is why the planet's unseen Government decided that mediumship should be brought from the clergy into the public square so that the notion of eternity, through the survival of the soul, would awaken the anesthetized mind of the populace. That is how Jesus is reappearing to us now – not as a founder of rituals and dogmatic boundaries, but in his true nature as the Redeemer of the Human Soul. The instrument of God par excellence, he utilized mediumship to light up his Doctrine of Love. In healing the sick and pacifying the afflicted, he often came in contact with the so-called dead, some of whom were nothing but suffering souls vampirizing the obsessed of many kinds. Besides talking with Moses materialized on Mt. Tabor, he himself is the great resurrected one, bequeathing humankind the empty tomb and accompanying his disciples with unblemished love so that they could continue their apostleship of blessings."

Hilario smiled like a student satisfied with the lesson and said:

"Ah yes! I think I'm starting to get it."

The work of the meeting was coming to a close.

Aulus sensed that Gabriel was about to write a closing message and respectfully asked him to address a few concepts regarding mediumship, to which the supervisor kindly acquiesced.

Dona Ambrosina had paused briefly to recuperate.

The meeting's director asked for silence in order to end the night's work, and as soon as the group reverently quieted down, Gabriel took control of the medium's mind, and holding her arm, wrote speedily.

In just a few minutes, his message was finished.

The medium stood and read it aloud:

"Dear friends, you must not seek in mediumship the false key to certain inappropriate arrangements, but rather the right pathway for our adjustment to the Greater Life.

"In grasping this truth, we need to renew our concepts concerning mediums, so that we do not make our fellow brothers and sisters oracles and fortunetellers, thus forgetting the duties of our own spiritual growth.

"Symbolically, Spiritism is Jesus returning to the world, inviting us to individual growth through constructive and incessant work.

"According to the laws of cooperation, it is right to accept the loving hand offered to us for the journey of salvation, but we mustn't forget that each of us bears core problems and non-transferable needs.

"Whether incarnate or discarnate, we all walk a wide field of experiences and trials that are in harmony with the imperatives of our growth toward immortality.

"Therefore, let's neither attribute to mediums obligations that are our own, nor expect miraculous functions from mediumship. We ourselves are responsible for the arduous effort of our own ascension with regard to the responsibilities that our higher understanding imposes on us.

"In light of our assertions, you may ask, in keeping with the old habits that characterize our mental laziness on earth: If Spiritism and mediumship do not resolve life's enigmas completely, what are they doing in the religious sanctuary of humankind?

"We will reply that in Spiritism and mediumship we can rediscover the pure thought of Christ, helping us comprehend for a broader discernment of reality. In them, we find precise information regarding the law of compensation, explaining afflictive problems of the soul, destiny and suffering, enabling us to perceive somehow the infinite dimensions toward which we are evolving. And above all, we owe to them the light to overcome the dark labyrinths of death in order to finally connect with the true notions of cosmic consciousness.

"Once such formulas of reasoning are attained, we will ask you in turn: Do you think it insignificant to reveal the greatness of Justice? Do you believe it to be of no consequence to unveil life in its limitless facets of evolution and eternity?

"So, let us revere Spiritism and mediumship as two living altars in the temple of faith, on which we can contemplate the sphere of earthly cogitations from a higher perspective, and finally understand that the glory reserved for the human spirit is sublime and infinite in the Divine Kingdom of the Universe."

The psychographed communication addressed other matters, and after its reading, a brief prayer of acknowledgement followed. While the assistants returned to their conversations, Hilario and I entered into a deep introspection to better learn and meditate, in light of the concepts we had heard.

19
Telepathic Domination

We were preparing to say our goodbyes when a pleasant discarnate woman approached us to compliment the Assistant with respectful affection.

Aulus introduced us.

"This is our sister Teonilia, one of the diligent workers in our assistance endeavors."

The new friend kindly returned our greeting and explained to Aulus what had brought her there.

She told us that Anesia, a devoted coworker at the institution, was going through very hard times.

In addition to the usual concerns of raising her three daughters and the assistance she had to give her sick mother, who was on the verge of discarnating, Anesia was also experiencing a tremendous inner struggle. Her husband Jovino was now strangely infatuated with another woman. He had become carelessly negligent toward his domestic sanctuary's obligations. He seemed completely disinterested in her and their daughters.

It was as if he had regressed to the wild extravagances of his early youth, as if he had never embraced the mission of being a father.

Day and night he let himself be dominated by the thoughts of this new woman who had ensnared him in her trap of enticing charms.

At home, while at work or out on the street, she would always take over his unvigilant mind.

The poor wretch had become truly obsessed under the constant effects of the woman who anesthetized his sense of responsibility with himself.

Couldn't Aulus do something?

Wouldn't it be best to remove such an influence, like a lesion is extirpated through surgery?

The Assistant listened patiently and then spoke concisely:

"I know Anesia and I hold her in high esteem. For months now I haven't been able to visit her as I had wished. Of course, I won't deny her my fraternal assistance, but it wouldn't be appropriate to take drastic measures without a close look at the matter. We all know that, under any circumstance, obsession among discarnates or incarnates is a mental illness that often requires lengthy treatment. Who knows if poor Jovino is not in the condition of a hypnotized bird, in spite of the portliness that gives him the appearance of strength in the physical realm?"

"From what I can tell," remarked Teonilia, "I see only a man dedicated to his work, threatened by a perverse woman."

"Oh, no!" interrupted Aulus tolerantly. "Don't cubbyhole her like that. Above all, we must accept her as our unfortunate sister."

"Yes, yes ... I agree," exclaimed Teonilia, readjusting her attitude. "But at any rate, I'm begging for your charitable intercession. Anesia has been a providential coworker and I wouldn't be happy doing nothing to help her."

"We shall do all we can within our possibilities, but it is crucial for us to analyze the past in order to find the roots of this undue relationship."

And giving his voice a grave tone, the Assistant asked:

"Mightn't Jovino be returning to the recollections of his past? Mightn't this be a trial that our friend outlined for his own conscience with redemptive purposes, and which he cannot now resist?"

Teonilia made a gesture of silent humility while Aulus held her shoulders:

"Let's be optimistic and confident. Tomorrow at nightfall, you can count on us coming to Anesia's home. We'll study the situation more closely to see what we can do."

Our friend expressed her gratitude and said goodbye with a smile.

Alone with us as we returned to our temple of work and study, Aulus said this was another opportunity to continue our observations. Of course, the issue was tied to a problem of influence, and we would get the chance to examine important mediumistic phenomena in the common experience of many people.

At the agreed time, we met the next day to make the trip.

We arrived at nightfall.

Teonilia was waiting for us at the entrance of a comfortable, yet not luxurious home.

A small rose garden near the doorway spoke silently of the beautiful sentiments of its residents.

Guided by our friend, we went in.

The family was having dinner.

A young woman was lovingly tending to a handsome older gentleman. At his side were three girls, the youngest of whom appeared to be fourteen or fifteen.

The previous evening's conversation didn't need any more information, but Aulus explained with more detail:

"These are Anesia and Jovino, and their three daughters, Marcina, Marta and Marcia."

The family conversation was affectionate, but Jovino seemed grumpy. The children's sweet remarks didn't elicit the faintest smile. Nonetheless, the more the father showed his annoyance, the more pleasant and tender the mother became, encouraging the two older daughters to talk about humorous incidents at the trinket shop where they both worked.

After dinner, Anesia lovingly said to the youngest:

"Marcia, my dear, go to grandma's room and wait for me. She's sick and shouldn't be alone."

The young girl gladly obeyed, and a few moments later, Marcina and Marta went into the next room talking to each other.

Dona Anesia silently tidied up the kitchen, while her husband sat in an armchair, engrossed in the evening paper. Noticing that Jovino was getting up to leave, she gave him an anxious look and asked delicately:

"Should we wait up for you tonight?"

"Tonight? Tonight?" repeated Jovino without looking at her.

The lively dialog continued.

"Yes, some time later tonight; we'll say our prayers together."

"Prayers? What for?"

"Honestly, Jovino, I believe in the power of prayer and I don't think we have ever needed it as much as we do right now for peace in our home."

"I don't agree."

And with a strange smile, he continued sarcastically:

"I don't have time for your taboos. I have commitments to keep. I'm in the middle of examining a big business deal with some friends."

Just then, a surprising image of a woman appeared before his eyes, as if projected upon him from a distance, appearing and disappearing intermittently.

Jovino became more distracted, more annoyed.

He looked at his wife with ironic indifference, demonstrating incomparable spiritual hardness.

Intrigued by these circumstances, we heard Anesia, who was being embraced by Teonilia, saying almost pleadingly:

"Jovino, wouldn't you agree that we have grown apart, when we need to be closer?"

"Oh come on! Drop the sentimentality. Your concern would have been proper twenty years ago when we were just foolish students!"

"No, that's not it ... I'm worried about our home and our daughters."

"As for me, I don't see any reason to torture myself. I believe our home is well provided for and I'm not negligent about our family interests. My business is moving. I need the money and that's why I don't have time to waste on religious pieties and pleas to a God who obviously must be quite happy living in Heaven, without having to trouble himself with this world."

Anesia was about to respond, but her husband's attitude was so blatantly mocking that she thought it best to keep still.

After straightening the knot on his bright-colored tie, Jovino slammed the door on his way out.

His humiliated wife fell in tears into an old armchair and started to articulate thoughts without words.

"Business! Business! ... It's just one lie after another! Another woman – that's what it is! ... A heartless woman who can't see our problems! ... Debts, work, exhaustion! Our home mortgaged; my old mother dying! ... Our girls fighting early in life for their own subsistence!"

While her thoughts became audible to us as they radiated throughout the small room, we saw again the same image of the woman that came into sight before Jovino. She appeared and reappeared around the sad wife, as if piercing her heart with invisible arrows of anguish, because Anesia now felt inexplicably disconcerted.

She couldn't see the strange and undesirable visit with her eyes, but she sensed its presence as an uncontrollable mental tribulation. Suddenly, she went from peaceable meditation to tempestuous thoughts.

"Yes, I remember her," she now reflected in complete desperation. "I know her! She's a doll of wickedness ... She's been causing trouble in our home for a long time. Jovino has changed ... Little by little he's abandoning us. He even seems to hate prayer ... Ah! What a horrible creature, an enemy like that who has worked her way into our lives like a treacherous snake! If I could, I would crush her under my feet, but nowadays I have a religious faith that guards my heart against violence."

However, as Anesia talked to herself in terms of revenge, the image projected from afar would come closer with more intensity, as if materializing itself in the ambient to inculcate greater discomfort.

The woman who dominated Jovino's spirit emerged visibly materialized before our eyes.

Both women, now avowed enemies, began their mental battle.

Bitter memories, harsh words, mutual accusations.

The tormented wife started to feel unpleasant physical sensations.

Blood rushed to her head, imposing a painful headache.

The more her rebellious and bitter thoughts expanded, the more her physical imbalance increased.

Teonilia embraced her lovingly and informed Aulus:

"This conflict has been repeating itself every day for many weeks now. I fear for our friend's health."

Aulus quickly began giving her magnetic passes of relief and the strange manifestations began diminishing until they disappeared completely.

After finishing Anesia's relative readjustment, and noticing our curiosity, the Assistant explained:

"Jovino is under an imperious telepathic domination, to which he surrendered easily. Considering that husband and wife breathe in a system of mutual influence, the effect that Jovino is suffering also involves Anesia, striking her in a lamentable manner because the poor woman hasn't been able to immunize herself with the benefits of unconditional forgiveness."

Intrigued, Hilario asked:

"Is this a common phenomenon?"

"Quite common. It's the influence that incarnate souls have on each other, which sometimes becomes a dangerous obsession. Millions of homes may be compared to trench warfare, where thoughts fight thoughts, taking on the most varied forms of anguish and repulsion."

"And could we include the matter in the realms of mediumship?"

"Completely, and to which we must add the phenomenon of attunement. Many types of mental alienation originate there. Quite often, within the same home, family or institution, deadly enemies from the past meet again. Called by the Higher Realms to reconcile, they rarely manage to overcome their mutual aversion, passionately nourishing inside themselves the toxic rays of antipathy, which become concentrated and turn into a magnetic venom capable of provoking infirmity and death. For that to happen, the mutual persecution doesn't even have to manifest itself in visible battles. All it takes are the silent vibrations of cruelty and spite, hatred and jealousy, violence and despair, which, fed by each party, constitute destructive corrosives."

After a brief pause, the Assistant continued:

"Thought exteriorizes and projects itself, forming images and suggestions that it flings toward the objectives it wishes to reach. When benign and edifying, it conforms to the Laws that rule us, creating harmony and happiness. However, when it is unbalanced and depressing, it establishes affliction and ruin. Mental chemistry is at the base of all transformations because we really do evolve in profound telepathic communion with all the incarnates or discarnates that are attuned to us."

"And how can we solve the problem of antipathy against us?" asked Hilario.

Aulus smiled and replied:

"The best way to put out a fire is to deny it fuel. Active fraternity is always the effective remedy for problems of this nature. That is why Christ advised us to love our enemies, to help those who persecute us and to pray for those who slander us. They are essential attitudes for ensuring our peace and victory."

Just then, Anesia checked her watch and stood up.

It was 8:00 p.m.

It was time for her prayers with her ailing mother. We accompanied her attentively in order to pray also.

20
Mediumship and Prayer

In a small room, a woman of about seventy had severe shortness of breath.

Little Marcia was waving an improvised fan, trying to give her some fresh air.

However, an unpleasant-looking spirit with a strange look of disturbance and suffering was clinging to her, increasing her physical torment.

It was a discarnate man exhibiting obvious mental alienation.

As Anesia sat down next to the ill woman with exceeding tenderness, trying to forget her own problems in order to help her, Aulus informed us:

"This is our sister Elisa. She is in the final hours of being freed from her physical body."

"And this man in such a sad condition at her bedside?" asked Hilario, indicating the spirit, who was unaware of our presence.

"He's the unfortunate son of our elderly friend. He left the physical experience many years ago. He had the misfortune of wallowing in the vice of drunkenness and was murdered on a night of excess. His mother, however, remembers him as a hero, and by evoking him incessantly, she keeps the poor wretch at her bedside."

"But why?!"

The Assistant changed his tone of voice and recommended we stay serene, that we would analyze the case some other time. Anesia's problem took precedence.

With a fatigued face, the poor woman was soothing the patient with words of love, but Dona Elisa seemed deranged, distant...

Anesia started to weep.

"Why the tears, Mommy? Grandma hasn't gotten any worse."

Marcia's soft voice resounded in the room with ineffable concern.

Far from grasping her mother's torment, the girl gave her a hug and asked her to pray.

Dona Anesia wanted her older daughters to be there too, but Marcina and Marta said that they would have to leave shortly to go to a coworker's birthday party.

Anesia sat close to the patient, and with her daughter's full attention, she began a heartfelt prayer.

As she prayed, a profound change took place inside her. The arrows of sadness that had been piercing her soul disappeared before rays of soft light coming from her heart. At that moment, as if a light had come on in complete darkness, several discarnate sufferers entered the room, approaching her like patients asking for medication.

None of them noticed our presence, and because of our silent curiosity, Aulus explained:

"These are spirits that are still at the same vibratory level they had when incarnate. In their present state, they readjust themselves more quickly with the help from incarnates, within whose range of impressions they still live. All those who are in such a state, within the radius of action of Anesia's prayers, receive the touch of spirituality that emanates from the prayers. If they are sensitive to the good or are eager for inner renewal, they respond readily to the lofty appeal that reaches them. They quickly follow the prayer, from whose sublime power they receive enlightenment, consolation, help and benefit."

"What value there is in a small act of faith!"

The Assistant patted Hilario's head and agreed:

"Yes, earth's people have created enormous complications on their pathway; however, death obliges them to return to simplicity in order to regenerate their lives."

At this point, Anesia opened her favorite book of Gospel meditations. She thought she was acting at random, but the subject matter was actually chosen by Teonilia, who kindly watched over her.

Surprised, Anesia noticed that the text described the necessity to work and forgive.

Docile, responding to her spirit mentor's influence, Jovino's wife began to talk wisely about the need for work and constructive tolerance on behalf of strengthening the good.

Without her even being aware of it, her flowing and soft voice transmitted Teonilia's thoughts as Teonilia tried to soothe her tormented heart.

During a lengthy pause, Marcia said wisely:

"Keep going, mommy! Keep going ... I get the feeling that there is a big crowd here."

Without realizing that she was preaching mostly to herself, Anesia continued:

"Yes, dear, we're alone because grandma is really tired and can't hear us. But that is only what it looks like. There are a whole lot of discarnate brothers and sisters here with us, listening to our prayer."

And she continued her commentary, which effectively gave courage to the spirits around her, who longed for the light as well as peace and moral reform.

After they had finished, Marcia kissed her mother goodbye. She had to get to sleep because of school the next day.

After loving recommendations to the girl, Anesia was left alone with her half-conscious mother.

She stroked her pale, wrinkled face, fixed her sweaty head on the pillows and stretched out beside her as if trying to think.

Aulus gestured to Teonilia and exclaimed:

"This is the right time."

Cautiously, they both began applying passes to her head, concentrating magnetic energy along the cortical cells.

Anesia felt overcome by a gentle hypnosis, which she didn't fight, attributing it to weariness.

After a few moments, she left her sleeping body and came to meet us in an almost natural disengagement.

She didn't seem as coherent on our plane as we would have liked, however.

Focused on her love for her husband, she made him her obsessing preoccupation. She recognized Teonilia and Aulus as benefactors, and cast us a meaningful look of empathy. But she appeared confused and afflicted ... She wanted to see her husband, to hear her husband...

The Assistant decided to grant her wish.

Supported on Teonilia's arms, she headed off as if she had known beforehand the details of where to find him.

Aulus explained that souls who live in close association are linked to one another by magnetic ties that overcome obstacles and distances.

In a large room of a nightclub, we found Jovino and the woman who had made herself known to us telepathically. Part of a happy group, they displayed a deep intimacy.

Diverse spirits surrounded the group, forming a harmful circle of vampires who didn't register our presence.

The party was engrossed in unedifying conversation.

Upon finding her husband in such a situation, Anesia let out a painful scream and fell into tears.

Followed by us, she ran out to the street. As soon as we were outside in the light night air, the Assistant embraced her paternally.

Noticing that she had composed herself somewhat – despite the suffering transfiguring her face – he said to her with extreme tenderness:

"Dear sister, calm down. You prayed for spiritual assistance and we are here to offer you solidarity. Courage! Don't lose hope!"

"Hope?" replied the poor woman in tears. "I'm being cheated on, miserably cheated on..."

Their conversation continued expressively and emotionally.

"Cheated on by whom?"

"My husband. He broke his marriage vows."

"But do you think that marriage is a simple walk in the garden of the flesh? Did you think that marriage was merely the music of illusion immortalized in time? My dear friend, the home is a school where souls come together for their own regeneration, aimed at the perfection that is ours in the future. Don't you know that schools have both teachers and students? Don't you know that the more advanced ones should help the less advanced?"

Called to her senses, Anesia stopped her complaining. Nonetheless, after gazing at Aulus with deep trust, she stated sadly:

"But Jovino..."

Aulus interrupted:

"Are you forgetting that your husband needs your love and understanding now more than ever? A wife shouldn't always see her husband as the man she loves dearly, but as a spiritual son in need of understanding and sacrifice in order to grow. Likewise, a husband cannot always regard his wife as the flower of his early dreams, but as a daughter of his heart in need of his tolerance and kindness in order to be led from the darkness to the light. Anesia, love is not just the rosy and sweet experience of satisfied sex. It is a light that shines more brightly than that, inspiring selflessness and unconditional forgiveness on behalf of those we love. Jovino is a plant that the Lord has entrusted into your care-giving hands. It is understandable that the plant might be attacked by parasites or deadly worms; however, there is no reason to fear if the gardener is watchful."

At this point of Aulus's wonderful exhortation, Anesia turned to him like a patient holding on to her doctor, and begged:

"Yes, yes ... I know that ... but please don't leave me alone ... I'm brokenhearted. What can I do about that woman controlling him? I see her as the cause of trouble and bitterness in our home ... She's like a diabolic spirit, fascinating and destroying him."

"You shouldn't refer to her with such harsh words. She, too, is our sister, a victim of regrettable errors!"

"But how can I accept her? I can see her evil influence ... She's like an invisible serpent bringing dreadful monsters with her into our house ... Our home has turned into a hell where we can no longer understand each other ... All is failure, disharmony and insecurity ... What to do with such a creature?"

"We must feel compassion towards her. Her awakening will be truly painful."

"Compassion?"

"What reprisal could be better?"

"Wouldn't it be better to get her to right her wrongs? Wouldn't it be better to relegate her to the darkness she deserves?"

Aulus held Anesia's trembling hand and continued.

"Let's not judge. According to the Master's lesson we now embrace, love should be our only approach toward our enemies. Revenge, Anesia, is the soul of black magic. Repaying evil for evil signifies the complete eclipse of reason. And under the empire of the darkness, what can we expect but blindness and death? No matter how afflictive the memory of this woman is, remember her in your prayers and meditations as a sister in need of our fraternal help. We have not yet re-acquired the full memory of our past, nor do we know what will happen to us in the future ... Who might she have been in the past? Someone we either helped or hurt? What will she be to us in the future? Our mother or daughter? Do not condemn! Hatred is like a fire that consumes everything; but love knows how to put out the fire and rebuild. According to the Law, goodness neutralizes evil, which transforms ultimately into a servant of the good itself. Even though everything seems to be conspiring against your happiness, continue to love and help, because, as we increase our moral merit, time will take charge of dispelling the darkness that visits us."

Like a resigned child, Anesia looked at her benefactor with limpid eyes as if to promise him obedience. Aulus embraced her and recommended:

"Go home and use humility and forgiveness, work and prayer, kindness and silence to defend its security. Your sick mother and your little girls need your pure love as much as Jovino, who will return, more experienced, to the refuge of your heart."

Anesia looked up at the sky constellated with light, said a prayer of praise and then went home.

We saw her wake up in her dense body, with soul renewed and almost happy.

She wiped the tears bathing her face and anxiously tried to recall every point of her conversation with us.

In reality, she could only recall fragmented memories, but she felt comforted, without rebelliousness or bitterness, as if intangible hands had washed her mind to give her a cleaner understanding of life.

She compassionately remembered Jovino and the woman who was hypnotizing him as needing her tolerance and pity.

A profound understanding blossomed in her mind. The comprehension as a sister had overcome the imbalance of the woman.

She thought to herself: What good is rebelliousness or discouragement when I should be thinking of looking after my home? By taking justice into my own hands, aren't I harming those who are the wealth of my heart?! Anywhere, scandal is always the ruin of all happiness ... Shouldn't I be thankful to God for being a worthy wife? Certainly the poor creature disturbing my husband has not yet awakened to responsibility and discernment. Therefore, she needs compassion and help, instead of criticism and bitterness...

Consoled and content, she proceeded to prepare her mother's medication.

Truly surprised, Hilario exalted the merits of prayer, to which Aulus added:

"In all of our interactions with incarnates, from tormented to glorious mediumship, prayer is a blessed light assimilating higher mental forces that aid us with our redemption or ascension."

Nodding toward the woman now at work in the room, my colleague remarked:

"So, we see in our friend a valuable mediumship under development."

"As is the case with millions of others," said the Assistant, "she possesses appreciable mediumistic resources that may be used for either good or evil. It's up to her to build within herself the strength of knowledge and vigilance in which to enjoy, in thought, the spiritual company more appropriate to her happiness.

"Through prayer she is seeking the solution to the enigmas that afflict her existence."

Aulus smiled and added:

"This is an invaluable lesson on prayer ... Anesia was unable to change the facts per se with prayer, but she was able to change herself. The present difficulties haven't been altered. Jovino is still in danger; their home is still threatened on its moral foundation; the old woman is close to death; however, our sister has garnered an impressive coefficient of energy to accept her trials, overcoming them with patience and valor. A transformed mind naturally transforms situations."

The Assistant stopped and reminded us that it was time to head back.

At Teonilia's request, he examined Dona Elisa and said that her discarnation was imminent.

I expressed my desire to examine her clinically, but Aulus reminded us that it was late, promising to return with us on the following night to assist the old woman.

21
Mediumship on the Death Bed

The following night we went back to Anesia's home with the particular purpose of assisting her sick mother.

Dona Elisa had taken a turn for the worse.

We found her greatly agitated, in the process of disengaging from her physical body.

The family doctor was examining her, displaying worry and discouragement.

His stethoscope examination revealed the difficult situation of the failing heart. In addition, the elevated blood urea nitrogen concentration was consistent with an alarming level of toxicity. He could foresee her physical endurance coming to a close; however, the patient's delirium puzzled him. Dona Elisa displayed a strange mental disturbance.

Overexcited and greatly afflicted, she said she was being chased by a man who was going to shoot her. She then called out for her son – who was already in the spirit realm – and said that she saw spiders and snakes at the foot of her bed.

In spite of the sticky sweat of those close to death and the extreme paleness that disfigured her face, she continued to make a supreme effort to speak.

The doctor called Anesia aside and told her that he expected the worst.

In response to the crisis, the patient should continue her medication, but the night would be trying. The uremia was spreading rapidly and her heart was like a ship out of control; thus, she could die at any moment.

Anesia listened to the doctor, wiping the tears that flowed from her eyes.

She bid him farewell and began to pray, trusting in Teonilia, who was watching over her like a selfless protector. Without being able to explain the soothing serenity that gradually took over her soul, she calmed down amid faith and patience, in the certainty that the assistance from the Higher Realm would not fail her. Though not grasping her devoted friend's tenderness, she received Teonilia's comforting expressions as sublime thoughts of hope and peace.

For a while, she contemplated the elderly woman crying for help in a muffled voice and gazed at her wide-open, expressionless eyes.

She was overcome with profound filial pity.

"Mom, do you feel any better now?"

Her mother took her hands as if she were a frightened child and whispered:

"I'm no better because that murderer's after me ... I can't get away from him ... I'm also surrounded by huge spiders ... What can you do to save me?!"

Soon thereafter, she screamed frightfully:

"Oh! The snakes! ... The snakes! ... They're hissing at me from the door! ... What'll become of me?"

She buried her face in her frail hands and tried to lift her body, moving her trembling head.

"Mom, calm down!" begged her daughter. "Let's trust in Providence. Jesus is our Watchful Friend. Why not hope for his protection? You'll get better ... Look closely. The room is peaceful."

The patient became somewhat calmer, but her eyes continued to show fear and mistrust. She asked Anesia to bend down and whispered in her ear.

"I feel that Olimpio is here ... My son has come down from Heaven to get me ... I'm sure of it ... It's my son, yes ... my son..."

The loving care-giver believed what she heard; but she knew that her brother's presence would not be desirable and asked her mother to pray with her. Wouldn't it be better to join together in prayer and ask for heavenly assistance?"

And while Anesia made herself the interpreter of Teonilia's assistance in her efforts to envelop the old woman in calming fluids, Aulus asked us to observe the interaction between the discarnate son and the poor dying mother.

Olimpio, the young man who had been murdered, clung to her like a parasitic plant asphyxiating a frail tree.

"In her tender love," explained Aulus, "our friend thinks that her son is a guardian angel, when in reality he is a wretch who allowed himself to be controlled by drunkenness even after losing his physical body. An impenitent alcoholic, he was shot one crazy night by a companion who was as drunk as he was. Separated from his body and already intensely taken over by 'delirium tremens', he didn't have the strength to mentalize his recovery and remained in the company of those who could prolong the excesses he enjoyed ... However, evoked by his mother's insistence, he ended up in this room, where he is ensnarled by her requests. However, as she gradually frees herself from her physical vessel, she is transferring her emotive field from the sphere of the flesh to that of the spirit, compulsorily suffering the pernicious influence of the spirit that she herself has called to her side using her will and her thoughts. In their situation, by necessity they are two minds attuned to the same band of impressions, because as weak as she is, she easily succumbs to the control of the young man, whose fear and disequilibrium are transfused into her submissive and loving soul."

Analyzing the phenomenon, I asked if this situation could be compared to mediumistic incorporation, as we know it.

"No doubt about it," confirmed the Assistant. "By attracting her son, in a profoundly passive state caused by her naturally-spent nerves and without the experience that would give her discernment and defense, Elisa is spontaneously assimilating the mental waves that portray his inner disharmony. As she slowly disincarnates, she is reflecting his remembrance of the past and the dreadful visions that are now so familiar, because away from his usual libations, our unfortunate friend is suffering the hallucinations common to victims of chronic alcoholism."

"Heavens!" exclaimed Hilario compassionately. "How can an old woman like this be submitted to such a trial? Isn't that a clamorous injustice?"

"I agree that this is an unfortunate scene," replied the Assistant. "But no one can break the laws that rule our lives. With her son here, Elisa has received what she was ardently hoping for. Of course, she may look like an old woman on death's doorstep, but in reality she is an immortal and responsible spirit, managing mental traits that are expressed and joined together according to clear and defined principles."

And after a brief pause, he continued:

"Many times we ask for what we don't know much about, and we get what we don't want. In the end, however, there is always a gain. The Lord enables us to get the precious benefits of experience from every situation and every problem."

Aulus didn't waste time on digressions.

He spoke quietly with Teonilia about the plans for the patient, and accepting our help, he detached the young man using advanced magnetism processes.

As soon as the wretched Olimpio was disconnected from his mother, we witnessed an interesting phenomenon. Dona Elisa had been talking animatedly but suddenly became completely prostrated, as if she had been restrained.

Observing our curiosity, Aulus explained:

"Her discarnate son was feeding her mental excitement, directly affecting her nervous system. Now she is limited to her own energies."

The patient emitted some guttural sounds and suddenly became quiet.

In vain, Anesia tried to get her to say something.

Dona Elisa could see and hear, but she couldn't articulate another word. In light of the acute pain in her chest, she tried unsuccessfully to move her arms but didn't have the strength.

Aulus rushed to administer calming passes, but without any palpable results.

"This is the final contraction of the coronaries," he exclaimed. "Elisa cannot last. The myocardium no longer responds to our magnetic influx. The angina has reached its end."

I could see that the dying woman wished to talk to her daughter, but uncontainable pain oppressed her chest.

Her tongue no longer obeyed her inner command.

She felt the time had come for her to make the journey to the grave ... As if a lightening bolt had struck her mental twilight – in one of those rare moments that are worth centuries for the soul – she quickly saw her past. Scenes from her childhood, teens and adulthood reappeared unexpectedly in the temple of her memory, as if inviting her to a scrupulous examination of her conscience.

She didn't waver.

Her moments in the flesh were numbered.

Incapable of communicating with her daughter, she wanted to say goodbye to her older sister who lived far away.

We watched her make a supreme effort to concentrate her thoughts to satisfy this one last desire.

In the meantime, Anesia, under Teonilia's influence, sensed that her mother had reached the end of her terrestrial existence. Embracing her lovingly, she prayed in silent tears.

The dying woman understood, but could only shed tears in reply.

Gazing at her daughter with a grief-filled and anxious look, Dona Elisa finally projected herself into our realm, albeit still held to her physical vessel by a cord of a silvery substance.

As her arms and legs became rigid, she had only one thought on her mind: saying goodbye to her last, living flesh-and-blood sister.

Enveloped in a wave of strength born of her own determination, she departed, lightly volitating in the direction of the city where her sister was living.

At Aulus's command, we followed her.

We covered dozens of miles instantaneously.

In the middle of the night, we stood beside her in a badly-lit room, in which a venerable old woman was sleeping peacefully.

"Matilde! Matilde!"

Elisa tried to awaken her in a hurry but couldn't. Conscious that she only had a few moments, she rapped on her sister's bed. Matilde woke up abruptly, immediately sensing her sister's influence.

Distraught, Dona Elisa started to talk to her. Dona Matilde didn't hear her with her physical ears but with her brain, through mental waves in the form of thoughts floating around her head.

She sat up anxiously and said to herself: "Elisa is dead."

Indicating the two sisters, the mentor explained:

"This is one of the usual types of communication in cases of death. Due to such repeated occurrences, the world's scientists have been forced to examine them. Some attribute the phenomena to telepathic transmissions, while others see them as a 'phenomenon of monition'[13]. But the Spiritist doctrine reduces them all to the pure and simple truth of being the direct communion between immortal souls."

"Can everyone," asked Hilario, "bid such farewells when leaving the earth if they so desire?"

"Yes, Hilario, you are correct when you say 'if they so desire', because such communications at the moment of death are only achieved by those who concentrate their mental power to do so."

We didn't have long to discuss the issue.

Once liberated from the desire that worried her soul, Dona Elisa headed back home as if her distant body were demanding her presence – much like what happens in a regular out-of-body experience.

Following her closely, we could see that she was less afflicted, although worn out.

Back in her room, following old habits, she tried to re-enter her physical body, as if reality were merely a strange nightmare. But exhausted and troubled, she hovered over her bed, still attached to her remains by the tenuous silver cord.

---

[13] An intimation of danger. www.merriam-webster.com. – Tr.

With her soul oppressed, the newly-discarnate resisted the desire to rest afflicting her mind. Indecisive and anguished, she couldn't tell if she was alive in the midst of death or dead in the midst of life.

Other spirit friends entered the room.

Aulus checked the time and added:

"Let's go. There's nothing more we can do here."

Hilario gazed at the silver cord connecting our just-freed friend and the rigid body, and asked:

"Can't we help dissolve that inconvenient cord?"

"No," explained the Assistant, "it has a specific function in rebalancing the soul. Death and birth are operations of the eternal life that require work and patience. Furthermore, there are spirits workers who specialize in the service of final deliverance. Theirs is the final touch."

Accompanying the Assistant, we left Anesia's home, where we had learned a priceless lesson.

22
Emerging from the Past

We went with Aulus to the second weekly meeting of the group presided over by Raul Silva, whose organization merited the sympathy and trust of our Instructor.

The team of workers had not changed its usual composition.

The small group of obsessed persons, however, was different this time.

Two women, followed by their respective husbands, and a worn-out gentleman were part of the group that would receive assistance.

The Spiritist center's mediums were involved in their loving task, using their abilities to help many spirits lost in darkness and suffering. Dona Celina's effective collaboration led the work.

After various problems related to the night's schedule were solved, one of the afflicted women fell into convulsive tears, exclaiming:

"Help me! Somebody, please help me!"

And pressing her chest with her hands, she added in a moving tone:

"Coward! Why stab a defenseless woman? Am I completely to blame? My blood will condemn your wretched name!"

With his usual serenity, Raul approached her and consoled her caringly:

"Dear sister, forgiveness is the remedy that restores our sick soul ... Don't let desperation overpower your strength! ... To hold on to offenses is to remain in darkness. Let's forget evil so that the light of the good may enter our path."

"Forget? Never! ... Do you know what it's like to have a knife plunged into your flesh? Do you know the wretchedness of a man who takes over your existence to cast you into misery, and then takes pleasure in spilling your blood?"

"Yes, yes ... no one's denying your right to justice, from what you're saying; but wouldn't it be wiser to wait for Divine Goodness to pronounce sentence? Who among us is without sin?"

"Wait? Wait?! I've been doing nothing *but* wait! In vain, have I been trying to regain my happiness ... No matter how much I try to cut off the past, I can't get rid of my memories. I'm like someone carrying a tomb of dead dreams in her chest ... All because of him ... All because of the wretch who ruined my life."

The poor creature broke into sobs while a discarnate man, not far away, gazed at her with inexpressible sadness.

Perplexed, Hilario and I looked questioningly at the Assistant, who perceived our puzzlement. The troubled patient immersed in afflictive suffering was not accompanied by the invisible woman she seemed to be personifying.

"I can't see the spirit whom our sister is communicating," said Hilario.

"Me either," I said in turn. "I can see a sad discarnate man nearby, but if he is telepathically linked to our friend here, surely the message would describe the words linked to a man, without the characteristics associated with a woman ... In fact, we can't see any magnetic ties that would indicate any teledynamic fluids acting on the medium's mind."

Aulus caressed the patient's tear-covered face, and as if he were analyzing her thoughts, he explained:

"We are dealing with our friend's past. The sorrow and bitterness, as well as the supposedly alien personality she's exteriorizing, all originate from herself ... Due to the proximity of a past enemy who continues to persecute her from our plane, she is reliving a dolorous experience that took place in a city in the Old World last century, causing her enduring melancholy."

"She recommended the struggle in the flesh in her present reincarnation filled with new hopes. However, as soon as she senses the presence of the spirit of her old persecutor, who is connected to her through the strong ties of love and hate, it disturbs her mental life in need of a fuller reeducation. This is a case that involves an invaluable lesson."

"So, that means..."

Hilario's sentence was left hanging in the air because Aulus completed his thought:

"It means that our sister has tied up a huge amount of resources from her emotive world around this past experience to the point that such mental crystallization has overpowered the biological shock of rebirth in the physical world and continues almost intact. Fixated on that memory, when the man who used to be her imprudent tormentor comes near, she begins acting as if she were still in the past that she insists on reviving. That is when she takes on the different personality, the one that refers to her former life."

Smiling paternally, he pondered:

"Unquestionably, at such times she is someone who has returned from the past to communicate with the present. Under the influence of the painful memories that assail her, she centralizes all her mnemonic resources solely on the neuralgic point where she has fixated her thought. To the ordinary psychiatrist, she is merely a candidate for insulin or electroshock therapy; but to us, she is a spiritual patient, a tormented conscience, demanding moral and educational assistance for her inner renewal, the only solid basis that will ensure her definitive readjustment."

I analyzed her carefully and concluded:

"Mediumistically speaking, this is an authentic case of animism[14]. Our friend believes she is incarnating a different personality, when, in fact, she is only exteriorizing her own inner world…"

"… So, could we classify this case as unconscious mystification[15]?" interrupted Hilario.

Aulus thought for a minute and responded:

"Many individuals working in the establishment of the New Era under the auspices of Spiritism are turning the animist theory into an unjustifiable constraint that paralyzes invaluable opportunities for accomplishing the good. Therefore, we cannot use the words 'unconscious or subconscious mystification' to label this phenomenon correctly. In reality, the manifestation derives directly from our friend's own sentiments flung back into the past, from where she gathers the depressing impressions that take her over and which she externalizes wherever she is at the

---

[14] "… I propose to designate by the word "animism" all intellectual and physical phenomena that suppose an extra-corporeal activity – or outside the limits of the physical body – and more especially all mediumistic phenomena that can be explained by an action performed by a living human being beyond his or her physical body. … Therefore, animic phenomena are effected under the 'extra-corporeal action of a living [incarnated human being.'" (free translation) Alexander Aksakow, *Animismo e Espiritismo* [Animism and Spiritism] (FEB, 1991). Please see also *The Mediums' Book*, by Allan Kardec, Ch. XIX: "The role of mediums in communications". – Tr.

[15] Pretending to be something it is not. – Tr.

time. The poor woman acts almost like a perfect somnambulist, for she concentrates fully on her past remembrances, as if she were focusing all the energies of her memory on one single wound, entirely unconcerned about the responsibilities of her present reincarnation. We are looking at a mentally ill person requiring our greatest attention for her recovery. To remedy her problem, however, complex diagnoses or mere technical definitions aren't enough unless coupled with the warmth of heartfelt assistance."

Aulus paused briefly to soothe the patient. As Raul Silva continued to instruct and console her, Aulus told us kindly:

"She should be treated with the same attention given to the suffering spirits who communicate. She, too, is an immortal spirit in need of our attention and understanding in order for her harmony to be restored. The idea of a mystification would perhaps lead us to a disrespectful attitude regarding her mental suffering. Hence, in such circumstances, we have to fill our hearts with love in order to understand and be of help. A counselor without fraternal tact would only aggravate her problem since under the pretext of serving the truth, he or she would perhaps impose an unsuitable corrective measure instead of providential assistance. First, it is necessary to remove the illness, and after that to strengthen the victim to enable her to defend herself. Fortunately, Raul assimilates the spiritual currents that prevail here and has become the ideal care-giver for situations like this."

Hilario, edified as much as I was with the lesson, asked respectfully:

"Can we consider her a medium nonetheless?"

"Why not? A defective vessel can be repaired and restored to service. Of course, patience and charity need to be activated to assist her. Our sister must be listened to in the condition she's in, as if she were, in fact, that unfortunate woman of bygone times. She must be received by us as such so that she can use the moral remedy we offer her and finally break from the past ... This would not be contradictory, because the former woman undoubtedly still exists within her. The old personality was not as eclipsed by dense matter as would have been desirable. She was reborn in the flesh without renewing herself in spirit."

The Assistant seemed to immerse his thoughts in the depths of his own consciousness, and then continued, as if speaking to himself:

"She is the portrayal of thousands of other souls! ... How many beggars drag around the tattered cloak of the ephemeral aristocracy they wore in the past! How many, enslaved by poverty and suffering, bring with them the vanity and pride of the powerful masters they once were in times past! ... How many souls, led to be born into the same family, travel from cradle to grave bearing invisible sores of aversion and hatred toward their own kin, who used to be their cruel adversaries in prior lives! ... All of us can fall into similar situations if we do not learn to cultivate forgetfulness of evil and advance continually in tandem with the good."

At this point, Raul Silva, as a skillful psychologist, invited the patient to the benefits of prayer.

It was up to her to beseech Heaven for the grace to forget. It was up to her to expunge the past from her mind in order to find peace. Highly moved, he invited her to say with him the sublime words of the Lord's Prayer.

The poor woman accompanied him meekly.

After the prayer, she seemed more peaceful.

Translating the Assistant's collaboration, Raul benevolently asked her to consider that, to find peace once again, it was important, above all, to forgive her enemies. In tears, the patient disconnected herself from the impressions of the past and returned to her normal state.

While she received comforting passes from Silva, the Assistant remarked:

"This is all the assistance we can give her for now. With the appropriate spiritual therapy, she will readjust herself little by little, regaining her self-control and preparing herself for invaluable mediumistic work later on."

We would have liked to continue analyzing the case. However, another female patient unexpectedly fell into an agitated trance and we had to proceed with our studies, making the best of it.

23
Fascination[16]

The woman had stood up in a weird manner. Spinning on her heels as if a motor were acting on her nerves, she fell into convulsions, inspiring pity.

She was under the control of perverse spirits of darkness, with one of them acting more strongly on her than the others. Winding himself around her, he seemed to want to put an end to her life.

Virtually howling like a wounded wolf, the poor woman screamed while thrashing around on the floor. A consternated Raul followed the scene while silently praying to Divine Goodness.

Coiling on the floor, she took on an animalistic appearance, albeit under the benevolent watch-care of the center's guards.

Aulus and brother Clementino used advanced magnetic resources to intervene in the deplorable duel, forcing the obsessor

[16] "... It refers to a delusion created directly by a spirit in the thought of a medium, which in a certain manner paralyzes his or her capacity to judge the quality of the communications. Fascinated mediums do not believe themselves to be deceived. These spirits manage to inspire them with a blind confidence that prevents them from realizing the deception and comprehending the absurdity [of how they act] ...." Allan Kardec, *The Mediums' Book*, Part Two, Ch. XXIII, #239. – Tr.

spirit to loosen his grip somewhat over the patient. Nonetheless, she continued to be dominated by him from a short distance.

After she was helped up to sit next to her husband, our instructor quickly explained:

"This is a complex case of fascination. Our sister is under the control of a dreadful discarnate hypnotizer, who is assisted by several fellow spirits involved in an intricate web of revenge. Under the impulsion of the hatred he casts over the unfortunate woman, his purpose is to humiliate her through the use of suggestion. If it weren't for the fraternal assistance she receives in this sanctuary of prayer, in trances such as this one, she would be a complete victim of lycanthropy[17]. Many spirits, perverted in crime, abuse their powers of intelligence, imposing a tiger-like cruelty on those still attuned to them by past debts. To such vampires we owe many dolorous cases of the mental pathologies in asylums, where numerous patients under intensive hypnotic action imitate the customs, positions and postures of various animals."

While the patient moaned weirdly, supported by her husband and Raul, an astonished Hilario asked:

"Is this heartbreaking phenomenon common?"

"It is quite common in the expiatory processes in which spirits, as partners in moral delinquency, sink to the vibratory level of the brute," explained Aulus while helping with assisting the patient, whose brain remained under the control of her insensitive persecutor like a toy in the hands of a child.

"And why not separate tormentor from victim once and for all?"

"Not so fast, Hilario!" pondered the Assistant. "We still don't know the fundamentals of the problem. Every obsession is founded on reciprocity. Let's recall the teaching of our Divine

---

[17] The delusion that one has become a wolf, or the werewolf transformation. www.medterms.com. – Tr.

Master. It isn't enough to pull up the tare: we need to know how deep its roots penetrate the soil together with the roots of the wheat, so that we don't ruin both at the same time. There is no pain without good reason. So, let's fulfill the law of cooperation without getting ahead of the Divine justice."

Under the guidance of the center's spirit mentor, Raul was trying to calm down the angry communicating spirit, reminding him of the advantages of forgiveness and inculcating the importance of humility and prayer.

Not wanting to lose the thread of the lesson, Hilario asked eagerly:

"But is verbal assistance enough for helping such desperate brothers?"

"We aren't offering them mere words, but more importantly, our sentiments. Every phrase spoken with love is a projection of our own selves. Thus, while the possibility of offering them premature liberation is not viable, we can still extend them our good will through words born in our hearts. After all, we too are in full need of redemption in Christ."

And in a highly significant tone, he added:

"In analyzing the past, to which we are all tied through bitter memories, we are patients in reciprocal assistance. It wouldn't be right to presume to pass definitive judgment either for or against anyone, because we are still in the position of having larger or smaller debts to liquidate."

Breaking off the conversation, our instructor focused on providing efficient assistance to the twosome in desperate combat.

For the fraternal care he was exemplifying, both patient and persecutor deserved the same treatment.

Aulus applied passes to unblock the patient's throat. Shortly thereafter, her tormentor started to speak gibberish through her. We could not understand the literal meaning.

However, through the thought waves that characterized his manifestation, we knew that he was brimming with hatred.

Raul Silva was getting the same impression through the harsh inflection of the voice with which the words were spoken and was trying to calm him down.

Observing the completely transfigured patient and noticing our silent curiosity, Aulus took a few minutes to examine the brains of both medium and communicating spirit, as if probing their innermost worlds. Then, he turned his attention back to us.

In light of Aulus's profound look of concern, before I could utter a word, Hilario asked in astonishment:

"To what cause can we attribute such a conflict?"

"I tried to look into their past to find out," responded Aulus sadly. "The roots of discord go back a long way. Despite our duty of not relating details in order not to give evil more weight, I can tell you that this enigma has persisted for over a millennium. Our unfortunate brother is speaking in an ancient dialect of old Tuscany. There, to satisfy the woman he obsesses today, he turned into a cruel strangler. He was a legionnaire of Hugh[18], the powerful duke of Provence in the 10th century ... From what I could gather from his dreadful memories ... he took part in the plundering at that time, during which, in order to try to please this woman – who did not return his devotion – he killed his own parents ... His heart is like a vase overflowing with bile."

Because the Assistant ceased his narrative, my colleague, naturally as interested as I was in knowing more, asked for more details. But Aulus suggested that we calm our yearning to ask further questions.

---

[18] Hugh of Arles was born sometime before 887, the son of Theobald of Arles and of Bertha, illegitimate daughter of Lothar II of Lotharingia. Elected King of Italy in 924, he relinquished his interests in Provence in 933 and died in 947. www.wordiq.com/definition/Hugh. – Tr.

To bring back those dreadful scenes, left behind long ago by these suffering souls, would edify no one.

They were two desperate hearts in the hell made by themselves. It wouldn't be appropriate to analyze further their crypt of fire and mire in the darkness of the past.

Returning my attention to our study, I asked about the issue of the language.

We were in Brazil, but the obsessed woman had spoken in a dead dialect.

"Why didn't she assimilate her obsessor's thought – which had taken over her brain in irrepressible waves – and transform the words into current Portuguese, as happened in numerous other processes of communication that we have observed?"

"This is a case of polyglot mediumship or xenoglossy[19]," explained the Assistant. "The mediumistic filter [the medium] and the spirit that utilizes it are so intensely attuned to each other that the passivity of the medium is completely under the control of the will that dominates it. As strange as it sounds, the obsessor is still ensconced in the habits that ruled his existence centuries ago; thus, in expressing himself through the medium, he uses mannerisms and phrases that used to be characteristic of him."

"But is this due to mediumship per se or to a deeper attunement?" asked Hilario.

"It's a matter of attunement."

"But if the patient had not shared the obsessor's earthly experience as a legitimate connection to his destiny, would the spirit still be able to use this dialect to communicate?"

"Positively not," explained Aulus. "In all cases of xenoglossy, it is essential to remember that the experiences from the past are brought forward into the present. In producing this kind of phenomenon, discarnates almost always interfere

---

[19] The ability to speak a language that one has never learned. – Tr.

through automatic impulses in the subconscious energies, but they do so exclusively through personalities they are attuned to from the past. When an illiterate medium begins to write under the control of a discarnate from our plane, it doesn't mean that the spirit messenger has miraculously removed the hindrances of ignorance. It merely shows that the psychographic medium has brought with him or her, from previous incarnations, the art of writing, acquired previously and stored in the memory, whose centers the discarnate spirit is able to manipulate."

Hilario, in his learner's posture, insisted:

"So we can conclude that if the patient were just a medium without this particular past, the spirit would not express himself through her in a cultural expression different than her own."

"Yes, that's right," approved the Assistant. "In mediumship, there is also the issue of attunement in chronological time."

And with a vague look, he stressed:

"This particular case can be somewhat compared to currents of water. Each kind has its own significance. Surface water is useful and has its peculiar enchantment, but only groundwater contains the wild or treated potential of the enormous latent forces that can be suitably utilized when brought to the surface."

The lesson was of great value, but it was necessary to return to the work of assistance.

Adding our efforts, we were able to separate tormentor from victim somewhat. According to Aulus, however, they were still united by magnetic fusion, even while apart.

Spirit workers from our sphere removed the obsessor spirit, steering him to a particular assistance organization.

Nonetheless, the patient continued screaming, saying that the dreadful strangler was about to choke her.

Applying comforting passes, Aulus explained:

"Now it's just a hallucinatory phenomenon. This is perfectly natural in such cases of fascination. Persecutor and persecuted are in a tight telepathic connection, acting and reacting mentally on each other."

The patient gradually settled down.

Once the outbursts had ended, I asked Aulus about the definite remedy for such a dolorous situation. He replied gravely:

"The patient is being prepared with a focus on a just solution to the case. She and the tormentor will soon become mother and son. There is no other alternative as a redemptive option. Divine energies of pure love will more intensely touch her sensitivity and she will practice the holy heroism of welcoming him into her arms."

Leaving us to our thoughts, he walked over to another person in need, while saying:

"God be praised for the glory of home life!"

24
Expiatory Struggle

Next to us, a gentleman sitting with the other patients was suddenly overcome by severe choreiform movements[20].

If it hadn't been for the chair he was sitting in, he would have been tossed to the ground.

He emitted groaning and grunting sounds, as if an invisible glove were strangling him.

Not far away, two unpleasant looking spirits were watching his movements, but without visibly acting magnetically to cause his nervous agitation.

The patient looked much older, but Aulus enlightened us:

"This is a poor brother involved in expiatory struggle. He is barely thirty years old in his present journey on the earth. Since infancy, due to his unfortunate behavior, he has endured the indirect contact of his morally delinquent companions from the past. And when he experiences the close influence of these wayward spirits,

---

[20] Involuntary, forcible, rapid, jerky movements that may be subtle or become confluent, markedly altering normal patterns of movement. www.online-medical-dictionary. org. – Tr.

whom he lingered with for quite some time before reincarnating, he reflects their noxious influence, giving in to hysterical fits that smother his joy of living. It has been a troublesome problem for the domestic sanctuary into which he was reborn. Ever since childhood, he has gone from doctor to doctor. Recently, he has undergone malaria, insulin and electroshock therapies, without any perceivable results. The painful and difficult treatments have taken their toll on his physical life. He looks like an old man, when he should be displaying youthful vigor."

While the pallid patient trembled, Aulus and brother Clementino applied magnetic assistance to quiet his disturbed body.

Once the paroxysmal incident ended, we noticed the patient to be sweaty and forgetful, as if he had been deaf to Raul Silva's prayers for divine help on his behalf.

After a few minutes, tranquility was completely restored in the room.

The meeting was coming to a close, but the young man remained listless and melancholic.

We could see varying degrees of hope and encouragement in everyone present, but not in him - he denoted torment and introversion.

With his usual tolerance, Aulus was willing to hear our questions.

"How should we diagnose our friend's case?" asked Hilario. "He didn't leave his body, and as far as we could tell, he didn't seem to assimilate the fluidic emissions from any inhabitant of our sphere ... Was the trance caused by some mediumistic process unknown to us?"

"Our brother's enigma is of a mental nature if we were to consider its pure and simple origin, but like other occurrences of a mediumistic nature, its roots lie in psychic sensitivity," clarified Aulus.

"Even so," I asked, "can we consider him a medium?"

"Not for now. For the time being, he is a patient in need of assistance; but once his disharmony is remedied, he will be able to cultivate invaluable mediumistic faculties, because illness in such cases is an important experience factor. Pain in our inner lives is like the plow on untilled land. Tearing and wounding, it offers the best resources for production."

"And the sickness itself?" asked Hilario, surprised. "Is it in the body or in the soul?"

"It is the imbalance of the soul reflected in the body," replied Aulus. And caressing the brow of the sad young man, he continued:

"Before his present immersion in the flesh, our atoning friend wandered for many years in a desolate region of darkness. There, he was the victim of cruel hypnotizers, with whom he was closely attuned due to the moral delinquency he had devoted himself to while on the earth. He suffered intensely and returned to earth with certain defects in his perispiritual organism. He suffers from hysteria[21], according to the proper definition of the word. Received by the heroism of a mother's heart and a father who was his partner in delinquency – and who today is undergoing his own bitter trials – he has been seeking his own recovery. At seven years of age, when his reincarnation became consolidated, he started feeling the disharmony he had brought over from the spirit world. Ever since then, he has struggled in the laborious, self-imposed regenerative process. Shackled to the disturbances in which he is enmeshed, he thinks he was born with a congenital defect. He feels incapable of any meaningful work. He feels defeated in the face of any struggle. He is only

---

[21] Historical term for a chronic, but fluctuating, disorder beginning in early life and characterized by recurrent and multiple somatic complaints not apparently due to physical illness. This diagnosis is not used in contemporary practice [the condition is currently termed conversion disorder]. www.online-medical-dictionary.org. – Tr.

happy when alone, when he nurtures the sickly thoughts emitted to his soul by his former companions in vice. In sum, he lives under deplorable, long-term pathological conditions of the nervous system, characterized by strange mental disturbances and sudden convulsions that have rendered him temporarily incapable of meaningful work."

The closing prayers invited us to observe silence.

After the meeting, Aulus offered to accompany the patient home and Clementino happily approved.

The young man seemed sedated, motionless...

After helping him through the streets for half an hour, we arrived at a simple suburban home.

At the young man's insistent call, a kindly old woman came to the door.

"Americo, my son, thank God you're home."

Maternal tenderness vibrated unmistakably in that clear and comforting voice.

His mother led him inside, where a young drunkard was swearing up and down.

Looking at him in concern, she said:

"Unfortunately, Marcio has gone overboard again."

And noticing Americo's listlessness, she added:

"But let's take care of you first."

The young man didn't argue.

He let himself be led by his mother and got under the covers in a small room in the back of the house.

Americo immediately went to sleep, emerging next to us in the natural out-of-body state. However, he did not sense our presence in the least. He registered only the mental disturbance that possessed him.

Terrified and fearful, he ran into a nearby small bedroom and flung himself to the side of an old paralytic, crying:

"Father, I'm all alone! Alone! ... Who'll help me? I'm afraid! So afraid!"

Attentive and calm, the sick old man sensed America's presence somewhat, showing in his face a pained expression as if he heard his son's complaints.

Aulus suggested that I sound out the old man's thoughts as he lay on the clean cot. I tuned in and could hear his mind talking to itself:

"Oh Lord, I feel surrounded by troubled spirits ... Who is here with me? Lord, give me the ability to understand your will and accept your purposes ... Please, do not forsake me! Old age, illness and poverty are so hard to bear as we approach death!"

And under the influence of the young man, whose thoughts he assimilated without perceiving it, he bowed his head and wept copiously.

Gazing at them meaningfully, the Assistant explained:

"They are father and son. Julio, America's father, was struck several years ago by a lower limb paralysis. He is now shackled to his bed, from where he still makes efforts to support his family with light work. Constrained by his trial and loneliness, he began reading and meditating. He learned the truth of reincarnation, found consolation and hope in the teachings of Spiritism, and consequently, has been able to live out his harsh days with resignation and fortitude."

Aware of our thirst for more information, the Assistant continued after a brief pause:

"Sustained by his wife's heroic devotion, he brought five children into the world: one, a young girl who had been his blessed sister in a former life, and the other four, including America, all boys hard to handle. Marcio, who we already met, is an alcoholic. Guilherme and Benicio are wasting their youth on nighttime extravagances. Laura is her parents' selfless companion, and Americo, the firstborn, is still far from recovering his complete equilibrium."

"Observing Julio in such a situation," interrupted Hilario, "we are led to imagine the problems that must come up."

"Undoubtedly, the expiation of this domestic group is harsh and painful ... In the not-too-distant past, today's paralytic was the head of a small gang of evildoers. Extremely greedy, he took refuge in a small homestead, from where he attacked unsuspecting travelers, dedicating himself to robbery and vagrancy... He managed to convince four of his friends to accompany him in the criminal adventures arising from his domineering greediness, and thus compromised their moral lives. Those four companions are now his sons receiving his new guidance, filling him with worry and sorrow. He once led them astray from the upright path and now seeks to restore them to the righteous path while he, himself, is in dire straits."

The old man's tormented resignation moved our innermost fibers.

Another incident grabbed our attention, however.

A young woman of noble and serene bearing entered the room in spirit, passing us by without noticing us. Supporting Americo, she led him out of the room.

The Assistant perceived our unspoken inquiry and explained:

"That's Laura, the benevolent daughter. Even while physically asleep, she doesn't forget to care for her sick father."

"Does she live here too?" asked my colleague, surprised.

"Yes, she sleeps in a nearby bedroom."

After administering vitalizing resources to the weeping patient, the Assistant added:

"When the physical body rests, the soul not always does likewise. On most occasions, it follows its own impulses. Those dedicated to the general good continue to work in the sowing and harvesting of love, while others, enmeshed in evil, tend to prolong during physical sleep the nightmares they have gotten themselves into..."

"From what we have been able to tell," said Hilario, "mediumistic phenomena in the home are ongoing."

"Indeed!" confirmed Aulus. "The thoughts of those under the same roof act and react upon one another in a particular way through unceasing currents of assimilation. Incarnates' influence on one another is usually much greater than one might think. Quite often during the corporeal existence, the obsessors trampling us are living and breathing right next to us, reincarnated in the same domestic environment. Likewise, there are protector spirits that help and uplift us, and they, too, take part in our everyday experiences. It is crucial to understand that, everywhere and above all, we live in spirit. For this reason, the interaction between souls – parents and children, spouses, brothers and sisters, loved ones, colleagues, and friends and foes – in the family sanctuary or in institutions of service is obligatory and ongoing, so to speak. Without realizing it, we absorb ideas and strength from one another."

We were about to leave, when Hilario, taking advantage of the occasion, asked inquisitively:

"But returning to Americo's case: recognizing him as a person suffering from hysteria[22], does he benefit by attending a meeting where other mediums are developing?"

"And why not?" responded the Assistant. "Progress is the work of cooperation. By dedicating himself to discipline, study, meditation and prayer, he will renew himself mentally, speeding his healing. He then will be able to cooperate in beneficial mediumistic endeavors. Every worthwhile effort, no matter how small, invariably receives the best response from life."

At this point, Aulus remembered tasks to be performed elsewhere and ended the invaluable lesson.

---

[22] Conversion disorder. – Tr.

25
Mental Fixation

On the way back, Hilario and I directed the conversation towards getting Aulus to teach us something about mental fixation.

I had noticed this phenomenon on many occasions and had tried to study it. However, in order to help my colleague, who was newer than I in the endeavors of the spirit world, I joined in, showing the utmost interest.

Hilario had been unable to disguise the astonishment that had overcome his soul ever since the manifestation of the strangler from Tuscany, and said in concern:

"Try as I might, I'm finding it very difficult to grasp the enigmas of the spirit's crystallization around certain situations and sentiments. How can the mind linger on particular impressions and hang on to them as if time were standing still? For example, let's take the case of that unfortunate friend who has been immobilized for centuries in his ideas of vengeance ... How could he have been in such a lamentable state for so many years without having reincarnated?"

Aulus listened attentively and pondered:

"We have to understand that, after the physical body dies, we continue developing the thoughts we cultivated during the corporeal experience. And we mustn't forget that the Law delineates universal principles that we cannot betray. Subordinated to evolution, how can we grow spiritually without obeying its order of harmony and progress? A fixed idea can trigger the indefinite stagnation in time of mental life.

"Let's symbolize the stage of the soul's reincarnation as being the valiant front in the battle for individual and collective growth, a battle in which the heart must arm itself with sanctifying ideas to win its self-sublimation, the greatest victory. The mind is the soldier in the battle. If it bravely wins, as soon as it is led to death's evaluation, it rises vertically to the front in the direction of the Higher Spheres and its triumph is expressed in its ascension to a higher level. But if it fails – and such a failure is nearly always the result of carelessness or rebelliousness – at death's assessment, it goes back horizontally to the rear, where it joins maladjusted spirits of every kind for an indefinite period of treatment. In these battles, the rear is the tormented zone of the neurotic, the crazed, the maimed, the wounded and the infirm of every sort."

In light of our interest in his exposition, Aulus continued after a brief pause:

"Of course, victorious legions do not forget those who have lagged behind; hence the missions of love and self-denial we see working diligently wherever there is disharmony and pain."

"And what about the soul's stagnancy?" asked my colleague, eager for knowledge.

"In our metaphor, we can define it quite accurately: time is always what we make of it. To better grasp the subject, let's remember that the hours on a clock do not vary, but they are not always the same in our mind. When we are happy, we don't even notice the minutes. When we are satisfying our ideals or innermost interests, the days fly by; however, in the company of suffering or apprehension, we feel like time has stopped completely. When we don't make an effort to overcome the slow motion of anguish, the afflictive or obsessive idea ends up corroding our mental life, leading us into fixation. Once we reach that level, time seems to stand still because in spirit we start to gravitate around the neuralgic point of our maladjustment. Any big inner disturbance – be it passion or disenchantment, cruelty or vengeance, jealousy or desperation – can immobilize us for an indefinite time in its web of darkness if we rebel against the imperative of incessant progress with the Supreme Good. Let's analyze further our symbol of combat. The inflexible clock indicates the same time for everyone; however, time is brief for those who triumphed and long for those who lost. For the triumphant, the days are happy and honorable, but for the defeated they are bitter and tear-filled. If we do not rid ourselves of thoughts of suffering and defeat through constant work for our renewal and progress, we become ghosts of affliction and discouragement, maimed in our highest hopes or trapped in our inner wounds. And when death surprises us in such conditions, emphasizing our subjective experience, if the soul does not make the heroic effort of supreme self-denial, it can easily get tangled up in the problems of fixation for years on end – sometimes even centuries – in the repetition of unpleasant reminiscences, living and nourishing itself on them. Indifferent to anything else but its own pain, idleness or hatred, the discarnate soul, lost in its own thoughts, is like an animal in the lethargic sleep of hibernation. It isolates itself from the outside world, vibrating solely around the hidden imbalance on which it strives. It no longer hears, sees or feels anything outside the deranged sphere of itself."

The subject matter was of immense interest for my personal observations.

On many occasions, I had closely probed sleeping consciences that were like spirit mummies after death. I reminded the Assistant of those cases, to which he replied:

"Indeed, during the habitual rest that immobilizes it after death, the mind stagnated in the forsaking of the Law suffers anguishing nightmares, awakening almost always in a state of full alienation that can persist for a long time, cultivating passionately the impressions in which it believes it can find its own happiness."

"And what is the most appropriate remedy?" I asked respectfully.

"Many of these disoriented souls," explained the Instructor, "finally tire of evil and seek regeneration on their own, whereas others awaken to the new responsibilities for self-readjustment during our work of assistance. They are the wounded soldiers who try to correspond to the missions of love that visit their places of recovery. They understand the imperative of the dignifying struggle to which they have been called, and assisting those who assist them, they return to the good battle, on whose frontlines they adjust to the service they are able to perform. Others, however, recalcitrant and rebellious, are gently obliged to return to the battle in order to rid themselves of their self-imposed lethargy. The experience of a difficult situation in a corporeal body is akin to a jolt of long duration, during which the soul is invited to recuperate. For that, we use the concourse of the subject's loved ones who harbor him or her in the family sanctuary."

"But in such cases, wouldn't compulsory reincarnation be like an act of violence?" asked Hilario, attentively.

"What do we do on the earth when an insane person becomes part of our family? Don't we assume the responsibility for his or her treatment? Would we wait for the deranged person's own decision regarding the measures needed to restore his or her mental stability? It is true that we have the duty to honor the free conscience that is capable of deciding for itself the various problems of the evolutionary struggle. However, when faced with an irresponsible and ill brother or sister, our assistance denotes loyal friendship, even if such intervention entails a pain-filled readjustment process on his or her behalf."

After a brief pause, Aulus continued:

"Reincarnation under such circumstances is like taking an inert patient to a certain friction machine for the necessary awakening. Intimately juxtaposed onto the cellular field, the soul is the happy prisoner of the physical body – whose atomic world it influences, and in turn, is influenced by – suffering the attrition meant for its recuperation."

These significant remarks invited us to meditate and learn.

Highly impressed, I said:

"Due to such fixations, we see spirits suffering deplorable amnesia. When they communicate with incarnate brothers and sisters, they don't have a precise recollection except for matters on which their worries are set, and when they exchange impressions with us, they seem like obstinate psychotics."

"Exactly. That is why they usually require a lot of gentleness in the way we handle them."

"And when they are led to reincarnate while imbalanced, do they suddenly return to reality?" I asked.

"Not always."

Changing the tone of his voice, the Assistant continued:

"In most cases, progress is very slow. We can verify this in the study of mentally impaired children, who convey dolorous enigmas for the world ... Only the extreme love of the parents and family can infuse warmth and vitality into such little ones, who often remain for many years in the dense matter as tormented members of society, enduring sufferings that seem unjustifiable and strange but which serve them as an effective remedy. It is also possible to observe the truth of our statements in so-called schizophrenics and paranoids who have lost their sense of proportion, harboring an erroneous concept of themselves. Nearly all of the congenital mental disturbances in incarnate individuals are related to fixations that preceded their return to the earth. In many cases, such incarnate spirits go from cradle to grave in a gradual process of recovery, experiencing beneficial jolts through human therapies and domestic demands, impositions of customs and social conflicts, which provide them the advantages of what we may regard as the 'extroversion' indispensable for the cure of their psychoses."

The conversation was instructive and suggested further study. However, other endeavors awaited the Assistant elsewhere, putting an end to our lesson.

26
Psychometry[23]

Our brief course was nearing its end.

Aulus didn't have time to grace us with further lessons. He was a worker committed to a wide variety of services,

Although Hilario and I understood that, we felt somewhat sad.

The Assistant, however, did all he could to keep up our usual enthusiasm.

We were crossing streets and squares when we found ourselves in front of a museum, where some late visitors were still lingering.

Wanting to take advantage of the time we had left for a few more observations and comments, Aulus invited us to enter, saying:

"It's possible to conduct very interesting studies in a place like this. You must have heard references to psychometry. In a good synonymic example, the term psychometry[24], as used

---

[23] Divination of facts concerning an object or its owner through contact with or proximity to the object. www.merriam-webster.com. – Tr.

[24] Field of study concerned with the theory and technique of psychological measurement, which includes the measurement of knowledge, abilities, attitudes, and

in experimental psychology, means 'to register, to evaluate mental activity,' but in mediumistic work it designates the faculty of reading impressions and memories by touching ordinary objects."

We crossed a wide doorway and once inside the building, we saw a large number of discarnate spirits coming and going, along with incarnates looking at articles of bygone times with much admiration.

"A lot of spirits with minds fixated on the past frequent places like this for the simple pleasure of recalling it," remarked the Assistant.

I noticed that a number of valuable objects, with a few exceptions, were enveloped in opaque fluids that formed a grayish or brownish mass in which luminous points were visible.

Noticing my curiosity, Aulus explained benevolently:

"All the objects framed by those fluidic substances are strongly remembered or frequently visited by those who used to possess them."

Not far away was a curious clock encircled by a luminous, whitish band.

Aulus suggested that I touch it, and almost instantly in my mind's eye I saw a lovely family meeting, in which an older couple was enjoying a conversation with four young people in the prime of their lives.

With that living picture projected in my inner mind, I examined the pleasant and stately room. The Austrian furniture added a sobriety and nobility to the ambient, which was decorated with vases of flowers and valuable paintings.

The clock was there as well, dominating the scene from an old wall, adorned with care.

---

personality traits. http://dictionary-psychology.com. – Tr.

Noting my surprise, the Assistant continued:

"I can perceive the image without directly touching the clock. It used to belong to a respectable 19th century family. It has retained the thought-forms of the couple that acquired it, and who from time to time visit the museum for the joy of remembering. The clock is an object animated by the reminiscences of its former owners, reminiscences that are rekindled in time through the spiritual ties they still hold for the loving circle they left behind."

Hilario touched the precious piece and said:

"That means that we are seeing images imprinted by them through vibrations..."

"Exactly," confirmed Aulus. "The clock is enveloped by the mental currents of those still attached to it, much like the copper is sensitized by the electric current while conducting electric energy. As we examine it in its present state, we are immediately tuning in to the memories of the people who cherish it."

Hilario thought for a few moments and remarked:

"So, if we were interested in meeting these people, an object like this one could be an intermediary for doing so."

"Yes, exactly," confirmed the Instructor. "We could use any object upon which their memory is focused. Anything that radiates from our thoughts would serve to facilitate this connection."

"The study of mental power is so very important," I remarked, greatly impressed.

Aulus smiled and commented:

"Thought spreads our own emanations everywhere it is projected. We leave spiritual vestiges wherever we project the rays of our mind, just as an animal leaves traces of its characteristic odor, making itself easily trackable by the dog's olfactory sensitivity. When freed from the dense body, our senses become more acute and thus we can easily perceive such phenomena within the sphere that limits our evolutionary aptitudes."

"That would lead us to believe," considered my colleague, "that we don't have the resources to register the thoughts of those more evolved than us."

"That's right. Those who have reached a level that we cannot even imagine have ascended to other realms, transcending our manner of being and expressing ourselves. Their thoughts vibrate on another frequency altogether. Of course, they can accompany and assist us, because it is the Law that spirits from a higher order can come down to spirits of a lower order whenever they want, but we, in turn, cannot go up to them."

Aulus reflected for a moment and continued:

"Let's use symbolism to grasp this more easily. What occurs between them and us also occurs between us and souls that are less evolved than we are. For example, we can care for the interests of primitive or backward tribes, but they cannot do the same for us. We can grasp their customs and knowledge, but they cannot understand a thing about our culture. Thought conditions us to the circle in which we have to or deserve to live, and only at the price of our own efforts or sure evolution are we able to improve it, overcoming limitations to enable it to vibrate in higher spheres."

The Assistant looked at us kindly and added:

"But let's avoid digressions not in tandem with our principal objectives."

"Let's say," I said in turn, "that we focus our attention on a more detailed examination. Would we be able to find out the history of the material that the clock is made of?"

"Without a doubt. It would demand more work and time, but it would be a perfectly viable undertaking."

"So, each object," concluded Hilario, "can be both an intermediary for contacting the persons interested in it and also a record of facts of nature."

"No more, no less," confirmed Aulus, sure of himself. "We have to remember that the paleontologist is able to reconstruct pieces of pre-historic fauna from a simple bone found at random. When we purify our sensitivity more intensely, we can find in simple abandoned objects expressive traits of people who possessed them or the occurrences they witnessed through the vibrations these objects retain."

And smiling, he added:

"Souls and objects, in the position they're situated, retain something of time and space, which are eternal in the memory of life."

Next, we stopped to study a beautiful painting from the 18th century, but which did not display any signs of a fluidic shroud.

In fact, it was an isolated treasure.

We couldn't establish any sort of external spiritual contact through it.

Aulus assumed his usual attitude of benevolent teacher and explained:

"If examined more deeply, this painting would be an interesting record, offering us information regarding its components; however, it would not work as an 'intermediary of spiritual relationships', because it has been completely forgotten by its creator and those who probably owned it."

We went a little farther.

In a large gallery, two gentlemen and three ladies were admiring a peculiar mirror. A discarnate young woman with an expression of profound sorrow was next to it.

One of the women praised the beauty of the mirror's frame, and the girl, like an angry guardian, approached her and touched her shoulders.

The woman shivered involuntarily from the unexpected chill and told her companions:

"There's a strange feeling like a funeral chamber. We'd better go."

After some good-humored remarks, the group followed her in another direction.

The spirit, who had not noticed our presence, seemed to be pleased with the solitude and, under a strange fascination, began gazing at the mirror.

Aulus touched her gently, then touched the object attentively and commented:

"Did you see what happened? Of the small group of visitors, the sister who felt the girl's touch possesses remarkable mediumistic sensitivity. If she were to cultivate her abilities and then probe the mirror, she would immediately establish contact with the girl still attached so madly to it. She would penetrate her secrets and would get to know her inner drama because she would immediately assimilate her mental wavelength, capturing its images."

Hilario was incapable of controlling the curiosity smoldering in his mind and asked about the girl. What was she doing here, in this tomb of memories? Why was she so anxiously interested in a simple mirror with little significance?

As if anticipating our question, the Assistant answered without hesitation:

"I touched the object myself to get information. This highly original mirror was entrusted to the girl by a boy who promised to marry her. I can see his romantic figure in her memories. He was the son of a French couple who had fled to Brazil during the French Revolution in 1791. A boy at the time, he grew up in Rio and became a man. He met the girl and won her heart. As they were thinking about marriage after having fallen deeply in love, the French couple, encouraged by Napoleon's success in Europe, decided to return home. The young man was decimated but didn't fight his father's orders. He bid his fiancée farewell and implored her to keep the mirror as a keepsake until he could come back and they would live happily ever after ... However, in France he was captured by the enchantments of another woman and never returned ... He quickly forgot his responsibilities and promises, and became indifferent. With her mind set on his promise, the poor girl continues to wait for him. The mirror is the pledge of her happiness. I can imagine the long journey she must have made in the course of time, watching over this keepsake as if it were her property until it finally came to rest in this museum."

"This matter," I ventured with concern, "compels us to reflect on the ancient tales about enchanted jewels."

"Yes, yes," said the Assistant. "The influence doesn't proceed from the jewels themselves, but from the forces that accompany them."

Hilario, who had been pondering the lesson, considered:

"What if someone were to acquire the object and take it home..."

"Of course," cut in the Instructor, "that person would be taking along the discarnate girl."

"Would that be fair?"

Aulus smiled lightly and said:

"Hilario, life never makes a mistake. It is possible that someone could come here, fall in love with the object, and want it."

"Who?"

"The young man who gave his word, causing the mental fixation of this poor creature; or the woman who lured him away from his promise. Reincarnated today or tomorrow, they might come here one day and take her as a daughter or companion to redeem their debt."

"But couldn't we assume the possibility that the girl could be attracted by some healing circle and rid herself of her disturbance?"

"Yes," agreed Aulus, "that's possible. Nonetheless, examining the harmony of the Law, the meeting of the three is inevitable. All the problems we create can be resolved only by us."

The conversation was invaluable, but our responsibilities compelled us to move on.

On our way out, we passed by the administrative office.

Seeing two empty chairs next to a small worktable, my colleague asked a question with the obvious intent to complete the lesson:

"I think that those two chairs are used by museum's employees ... If we sat in them, would we be able to make contact with the individuals who usually sit in them?"

"Yes, if we wanted that type of experience," said the Assistant.

"And what about incarnates? If someone uses objects that belong to someone else – clothes, beds or adornments – could he or she sense the thoughts of those who used them?"

"Perfectly well. However, in order to capture them, he or she would have to possess an acute psychic sensitivity. The marks of our individuality vibrate wherever we are, and through them we cause good or evil in those who come in contact with us."

"Is everything we have observed mediumship?!"

"Yes, in spite of such phenomena being listed by experimenters of the scientific world under different terminology, among them 'pragmatic cryptesthesia[25]', 'tactile metagnomy[26]', or 'telesthesia[27].

Leading us back onto the street, he concluded:

"In everything we see integration, affinity and attunement ... And there's one thing we can be sure of: through our thoughts we commune with one another in the plenitude of universal life."

---

[25] A hidden sensibility, a perception of things by a mechanism unknown to us of which we are cognizant only of its effects. It includes clairvoyance, premonition, monition, psychometry, dowsing, and telepathy. http://www.answers.com. – Tr.

[26] Unusual insight or intuitive perception. http://www.answers.com. – Tr.

[27] Perception from a distance through psychic rapport with the place or environment. http://www.answers.com. – Tr.

27
Mediumship Gone Astray

Nighttime had fallen completely as we entered a small room where a group of people was praying.

Several spirits were mingling there, but they were in terrible shape. They seemed less evolved than the men and women taking part in the meeting.

Only brother Cassio, an amiable and friendly guardian, to whom the Assistant introduced us, displayed a high moral standing.

His spiritual isolation was immediately obvious because neither the discarnates nor the incarnates were aware of his presence or received his thoughts.

At our Instructor's inquiries, he replied somewhat disheartened:

"So far, there has been no progress, in spite of the repeated appeals for renewal. We have provided Quintino with the best resources at our disposal – books, other printed materials, conversations from respectable sources, but all in vain ... Our stubborn friend is not yet taking stock of the huge responsibility he's assuming in leading a group like this."

Aulus tried to comfort him with a silent gesture of understanding and invited us to observe.

The room was full of dense, disagreeable fluids.

Spirits from our plane were communicating through two mediums. According to my first impressions, these spirits had become veritable servants of the group, possibly compensated for less-than-edifying services. Various servile and meddlesome spirits in the same conditions crowded around them.

Psychophony[28] was the main phenomenon in the gathering.

The mediums were out of their bodies but remained in the ambient, feeding on the emanations peculiar to them.

Raimundo, one of the communicating spirits under the complacent eye of the place's director, was conversing with a woman whose frivolous talk inspired pity.

"Raimundo," she was saying, "I need the money that has been piling up for months now at the Institute, of which I'm a harmed creditor. What can you tell me about the delay?"

"Be patient, dear sister," recommended the spirit. "We're working on it for you."

The conversation continued:

"The solution is urgent. You need to help me more effectively. Try to go to the office of that grumpy director and get the papers moving ... Do you want the addresses of the people that we need to influence?"

"No, no. I know them and where they live…"

"I can tell that you're distracted, Raimundo. You're not interested in my case with the necessary diligence."

"That's not it ... It's just that I've done all I can."

And while the woman lowered her voice to a whisper, a middle-aged gentleman addressed Teotonio, the other communicating spirit, complaining indiscreetly:

---

[28] Speaking mediumship. – Tr.

"Teotonio, how long do I still have to wait?"

Appearing to be dumbfounded by the question, the spirit meekly remained silent while the gentleman pressed the matter:

"I've been waiting for four months now for a favorable decision regarding the job I was promised. But nothing so far! ... Couldn't you take care of it?"

"What do you want me to do?"

"I know that the company's manager isn't favorable. Help me by getting him interested in the good resolution of my case."

In the meantime, Raimundo's attention was diverted by another woman who was asking him:

"My friend, I'm counting on your invaluable assistance. I'm a mother. I can't see my daughter accepting the marriage proposal of such a despicable man. It's an alarming situation at home. My husband can't stand him, and my rebellious daughter has been a torment. Couldn't you get that vulture out of our lives?"

Raimundo answered subserviently, while Quintino immediately requested everyone to pray together for the discarnates to get the strength to live up to the group's trust and fulfill the tasks asked of them.

The conversations and understandings continued between the communicating spirits and the place's clients, but I didn't pay them any further attention due to their shady aspect.

In heartrending circumstances, I had seen obsessors and spirits hardened in evil involved in tremendous conflicts, but nowhere had I felt the compassion I was feeling there as I saw healthy and lucid individuals viewing the communication with the spirit world as a system for criminal exploitation based on the conduct of least effort.

Would the men and women gathered there with such outlandish intentions have the courage to ask incarnate fellow beings for the kinds of services they were demanding from the spirits? Weren't they abusing prayer and mediumship to escape from their personal problems? Didn't they know enough to mobilize their brain, tongue, eyes, ears, hands and feet in the ennobling learning experience? What were they doing with their faith? Would it be right for a worker to leave to others the hoe that was his or her duty to hold and put into action in the fields of the world?

Aulus detected my bitter reflections and kindly hastened to comfort me.

"Any current study of mediumship – even one as brief as ours – would not be complete if we failed to examine the field of mediumship gone astray, where lazy incarnate and discarnate spirits live in an environment of mutual vampirization. As a matter of fact, they are a natural product of the defective ignorance in all types of humankind's places of worship. They abuse prayer as much as they despise the possibilities and opportunities of worthwhile work, looking for ephemeral advantages to accommodate themselves to indolence, in which they crystallize their childish whims."

"But will they go on like this forever?" I asked.

"Andre, your question misses the mark. You have enough experience to know that pain is the great administrator of Divine justice. Our lives are our great battle of evolution. Those who flee the sacrificial work of the frontlines will find pain in the rearguard. The spirit may fall into idleness, wrongly mobilizing its will. But the day of torment will finally arrive, compelling it to move and act to better understand the imperatives of progress. It's futile to flee eternity, because time, work's benefactor, is also inertia's executioner."

Hilario, who had been reflecting in silence nearby, asked worriedly:

"Why do our incarnate brothers and sisters get involved in such practices of least effort? There are so many lessons for spiritual improvement, so many appeals to dignify mediumship in the doctrinal guidelines of Spiritism! ... Why this lack of equilibrium?"

Aulus thought for a few moments and replied.

"Hilario, you have to remember that this is not in keeping with Spiritist teachings. We are witnessing mediumistic phenomena manipulated by idle minds inclined to debased exploitation wherever they are, and for that reason, deserving of our pity. We are fully aware of the fact that mediumistic phenomena are peculiar to all sanctuaries and all individuals. As for our friends' preference for living around discarnates still strongly bound to the sensorial field of physical life, incapable of a broader vision of the realities of the spirit ... well, that is understandable. It's always easier for ordinary individuals to work with subordinates or equals since working alongside the more evolved requires goodwill, discipline, right conduct and a firm desire to improve. We know that death is no miracle worker. Each person awakens beyond the grave in the spiritual position that he or she has sought out ... Ordinary individuals feel more at ease with spirits that flatter their passions and stimulate their appetites. When we find ourselves around more-evolved fellow beings, we feel compelled to educate ourselves, for they have already learned to sublimate their personal impulses, dedicating themselves to the incessant cultivation of the good."

"But isn't this an abuse of the incarnate individual? Isn't it a crime to prey on less-evolved discarnates?" asked Hilario.

"No question about it."

"Will such a crime go unpunished?"

Aulus displayed a slight expression of good humor and responded:

"Don't get too worried about it. When errors originate from well-intentioned ignorance, the Law provides the resources needed for the just enlightenment in space and time, since any genuine charity, in any circumstance, is always praiseworthy. On the other hand, if the abuse is deliberate, punishment is unavoidable."

He glanced over at the group's director and the mediums through whom the spirits were communicating, and added:

"Teotonio and Raimundo, as well as other discarnates like them around here, are actually more vampirized than vampirizing. Fascinated by Quintino's requests, as well as those of the mediums who support their unfortunate work, they follow in their steps like devoted students looking up to their mentors. In the event that they do not readjust to the good, then as soon as the director of the group and the mediums who copy his attitude discarnate, they will be assailed by the spirits they have enslaved asking for their guidance and help. Most probably, later on in the future to come, when victimizers and victims are reunited in the same family on earth as parents and children to settle accounts and readjust their attitudes, they will balance out the debts they had gotten themselves enmeshed in earlier."

Due to our silent wonder, the Assistant concluded:

"Each worthy deed receives its due payment, and each unworthy venture has its corresponding costs."

Aulus invited us to leave.

The ambient did not encourage further study and we had already assimilated the lesson to be learned.

28
Physical Effects

It was 8:00 p.m. earth time when we entered a small apartment where materialization phenomena would be performed.

Hilario and I didn't want to finish our week of study without following some work of this sort in the company of the Assistant.

On another occasion, we had observed this type of experience and had recorded our impressions.[29] However, Aulus's teachings were always instructive and valuable because of their moral foundations, so I was looking forward to hearing him explain the physical phenomena that we proposed to study.

The place set up for the work consisted of two rooms: a living room connected to a small bedroom.

The bedroom, turned into a study, accommodated the medium – still a young man – while fourteen apparently well-intentioned individuals were gathered in the living room. Two of

---

[29] See *Missionaries of the Light* – Spirit Auth. (International Spiritist Council, 2009, Chapter. 10) – Tr.

them were ailing women and the main reason for the meeting, since they wished to garner the friendly assistance of materialized spirits.

Indicating them, the Assistant spoke in a serious tone of voice:

"I brought you here to help the sick. There are many attempts at materializing forces from our plane, but with few exceptions, most of them are developed on foundations that are marked by the regrettable approaches of our incarnate brothers and sisters. At present, we see helping the sick as the only justification for an endeavor of this type, in addition to rare, essentially respectable and worthy experiments performed by the scientific world for the benefit of humankind."

We would like to have prolonged the explanation, but various workers were coming and going, implying that that evening's work was about to start.

The cleansing of the environment was underway.

The work required careful preparation.

According to our previous experiences, delicate instruments for the emission of healing rays were being placed in the room, while the ionization of the environment was effectuated with bactericidal devices.

As usually, some of the incarnates had not taken their responsibilities seriously and had brought with them toxic emanations arising from the abuse of nicotine, meat and alcohol, in addition to thought-forms that were unsuitable for the work to be carried out.

Attentive to the study, Aulus recommended that we focus our attention on the medium's room.

We obeyed.

It was bustling with activity.

Displaying great discipline, dozens of well-directed spirits were busy with the preparatory efforts.

The medium had already received effective aid in his organic field.

The digestive, circulatory and visceral systems had been stabilized.

We will forgo a more detailed description. As far as we were able, materialization has already deserved our meticulous examination concerning the substances, associations, resources and activities on the spirit plane.[30]

This time, we were interested in mediumship per se.

We were trying to analyze its behavior and its relations with regard to environment and people.

For that reason, as far as we could tell, there was no better occasion than this one, where we would have the sure collaboration of a competent and dedicated friend like the Assistant.

Once the lights were turned off and an opening prayer was said, the group, as usual, began singing some evangelical hymns to stabilize the vibrations in the room.

Discarnate coworkers extracted energies from persons and objects in the living room, as well as from nature outside. These energies were combined with elements from our sphere to turn the medium's room into an invaluable, complex laboratory.

As a result of the magnetic action by the spirit guides responsible for the task, the medium left his body in such a perfect way that the act looked to me like discarnation itself, because his physical body lay on the bed abandoned and inert as if it were a cocoon of flesh.

Under the control of technicians from our plane, it began to expel ectoplasm. This substance – a flexible paste much like a viscous, semi-liquid jelly – came out through every pore, and most abundantly through the natural orifices, particularly the mouth, nose and ears. A large amount also came from the chest

---

[30] See *Missionaries of the Light* – Spirit Auth.

area and extremities of the fingers. The ectoplasm, characterized by a unique, indescribable smell, flowed in reptilian movements to accumulate on the lower part of the medium's body, where it resembled a large, living and tremulous protoplasmic mass.

Spirit workers lent their loving assistance to the medium separated from his physical body as if he were a patient or a child.

Aulus kindly explained:

"The ectoplasm per se is as closely associated with the medium's thoughts as the energies of the developing fetus are connected to its mother's mind. Consequently, every precaution is being taken to assist him."

Hilario had been listening respectfully, and asked:

"Is such precaution due to the possibility of an inappropriate intervention by the medium in the procedures?"

"Exactly."

Aulus continued:

"If we could count on a better education of the medium, we would certainly have less to worry about because he himself would collaborate with us, freeing us from concerns and any possible setbacks. For the materialization of individuals and objects from our plane to be more complete, it would demand a more secure dematerialization of the medium and the incarnate fellow spirits that assist him. This is because no matter how much we devote ourselves to endeavors of this sort, we still depend on the cooperation of our incarnate friends. It is much like water, which, no matter how pure it may be, still depends on the good or bad condition of the channel through which it flows."

"That would seem to imply that the medium's thought can influence materialized forms even when such forms are under the strict control of workers from our realm."

"Yes," confirmed the Assistant. "Even if the medium cannot control such forms completely, he can interfere with their formation and projection, thereby jeopardizing the effort; hence the need for complete absence of personal interest on the part of all who devote themselves to such work."

Although satisfied, Hilario continued his line of thought:

"That being the case, the faculties of materialization do not entail any sort of privilege for those who have them."

"By no means."

And after a brief pause:

"In its literal sense, the very word *materialization* does not encourage any interpretation that would imply disaccord with the truth. To materialize means to embody. Thus, since mediumship does not imply sublimation but a means of serving, and furthermore, that death does not immediately purify the impure, how can we attribute sanctity to incarnate mediums or to those who communicate through them from the Beyond due to the simple fact that they mold passing forms between both planes?"

"Then, this materializing force..."

My companion didn't finish.

Aulus picked up on his thought and cut him short:

"This materializing force is like other forces that are manipulated in our tasks of interchange. It is independent of the character and moral quality of those who possess it and consists of emanations from the psychophysical world, of which cytoplasm is one of the sources of origin. In a few rare individuals, we find this energy in a higher percentage of exteriorization, but we know that it will be more abundant and accessible in the future, when the human community reaches a higher degree of spiritual maturity."

"So, until then..."

"Until then we will utilize such possibilities as someone who makes the most of an unripe fruit in special circumstances in life, experiencing a thousand unpleasant surprises as we collect it. In endeavors such as this one, we are not only subject to certain undesirable mediumistic interferences, but also to unedifying influences from our incarnate friends who are frankly inapt for work of this type."

Hilario was listening attentively to the lesson and asked further:

"Let's say that the medium has dishonorable interests, whether in matters of turbulent affections, excessive ambition, or personal points of view in the various areas of common passions ..."

After thinking for a moment, he asked:

"In that situation, could he or she influence these phenomena?"

"Without any doubt, either consciously or unconsciously."

"And the other participants of the group? If imbued with malevolent purposes, could they interfere?"

"Most certainly!"

"Then, why should we subject ourselves to such incapable factors?"

The Assistant's eyes shone expressively.

Patting my colleague on the back, he said sensibly:

"Don't say 'incapable factors'. Let's say 'insipient factors.' We can symbolize necessity as a parching thirst, and imperfect or poorly conducted mediumship as unclean water. At the lack of pure water, we can't hesitate: we utilize it in the condition we find it. And then what? We are patient with the spring, cleansing its polluted current little by little. Sublimated mediumship, through instruments that are worthy and conscientious of their mandate, is something eternal and divine that humankind is constructing. This is not the work of haste. Improvisation is not a foundation for sanctuaries of wisdom and love that are built to last."

My colleague and I smiled, enchanted with his understanding and tolerance.

In the room, a large mass of milky-silvery ectoplasm accumulated in abundance, in which a few dark grayish strands could be seen.

Technicians from our plane were carefully manipulating it.

Aulus surmised the operation and explained:

"That is the light, pliable material we need for the materialization. We can divide it into three essential elements: 1) A-fluids, representing the superior and subtle forces from our sphere; 2) B-fluids, defining the resources of the medium and the incarnates assisting him; and 3) C-fluids, made up of energies taken from nature. A-fluids can be the purest and C-fluids can be the most pliable; however, B-fluids, originated by the actuation of incarnates and the medium in particular, arc capable of spoiling our noblest plans. In extremely rare circles, where the elements of A-fluids receive full cooperation from the energies of B-fluids, materializations of a high order assume the finest characteristics to display the sublimity of the phenomena. However, where B-fluids predominate, our participation is considerably reduced, since our greatest possibilities will start to be channeled at the level of the less evolved forces from our plane. These forces are in tune with the potentialities of incarnate brothers and sisters and can take over their resources, invading their field of action and steering their psychic experiences towards regrettable disasters."

The explanation could not be clearer.

We were about to continue the discussion, but Garcez, one of the endeavor's spirit technicians, approached us to ask for Aulus's magnetic assistance.

The fluidic atmosphere in the room had become too dense. The small experimental jets of ectoplasmic force projected into the living room were returning to the medium's room with a high level of toxins of various kinds.

The fourteen people in the living room were fourteen types of different whims.

Not one of them had enough understanding of the efforts demanded from the spirit world, and instead of helping the medium, each person was overloading him with absurd requests.

Consequently, he didn't have enough serenity. He was like a rare animal poked with arrows – such were the improper thoughts shot in his direction.

"We won't be able to produce a materialization of the highest order," said the Assistant, somewhat worried.

"Not in the least," informed Garcez, disappointed. "The medium will remain out of his body, incorporating our nurse in order to assist the ill sisters – nothing more. We don't have the cooperation we need."

Aulus responded to the request and assisted with the magnetic transfer of a certain amount of energies from the medium's physical body to his perispiritual body, which became highly reanimated.

The body of dense matter on the bed fell into deep prostration, but the medium, in his perispirit, displayed greater vitality and greater lucidity.

Once the spirit workers enveloped him in a large ectoplasmic robe, the nurse joined him to guide his movements.

In spite of being outside his corporeal body, the medium was controlled by the nurse like a psychophonic medium. He was set apart only by his peculiar garment, structured with ectoplasmic materials crucial for his presence in the room, bombarded by perturbed and disquieting thoughts.

Watching him walk unsteadily, supported by the nurse as she moved him about for the work of assistance, Hilario whispered to the Assistant:

"Is the medium conscious?"

"While out of his body, yes, but he probably won't retain any memory once he returns."

Hilario ventured further:

"We can see that he is moving about in materialized garments under the nurse's guidance. But under these conditions, could he put the work at risk if he harbored any inappropriate desires?"

"Undoubtedly," replied Aulus. "He is under her control, but control doesn't mean nullification. Any improper impulse on his part would affect the work; hence the inappropriateness of this type of activity without a lofty moral objective.

Supported by the benevolent spirit, the healing medium reached the small living room, displaying the delicate garment similar to a moonlit tunic emitting a silvery light. But as he proceeded through the atmosphere reigning in the room, the clarity lessened until it nearly went out.

At our questioning look, the Assistant explained:

"The neuropsychic condition of the incarnates participating in the task does not help. They are absorbing our energies but are not in any way contributing to replenishing the expenditure of fluids so painstakingly prepared."

Aulus invited us to enter the living room.

In fact, continuous dark mental emissions were colliding with one another in a lamentable way.

Our incarnate friends seemed like unconscionable children.

Their thoughts were undesirable, expressing absurd requests in the apparent silence they were restlessly observing.

They were requesting the presence of discarnate loved ones, without considering the appropriateness or their merit for it; they were criticizing this or that particularity of the phenomenon; or they were tying their imagination to debased tribulations of their everyday lives.

The concourse of the good spirits was being received not as kindness from benefactors, but as a frivolous spectacle to be carried out by mere servants.

Even so, the workers from our plane were doing their best to ensure the success of the task.

The devoted nurse assisted the sick by treating them with healing rays. Several times, she left the room and then returned since at the mere proximity of any inadequate thoughts that would come in contact with her vibrations, the ectoplasmic matter would feel the effects and would darken under the bombardment of the participants' thought-forms.

When the healing work was over, a cheerful friend from our plane took a small amount of the medium's materialized energy in his hands and left. A few moments later, he returned with some flowers, which were distributed to the incarnates to calm their excitable minds.

Appeasing our curiosity, Aulus explained:

"This is an ordinary apportation, achieved with reduced aid of medianimic energies. Our friend here" he said as he pointed to the flowers' emissary, "took just a tiny amount of ectoplasmic energy, forming only small, superficial crystallizations of the thumb and index finger of both hands, to pick the flowers and bring them to us."

"It's interesting to note," said Hilario, "how easily ectoplasmic energy passes through dense matter. Utilizing it on his fingers, our colleague found no obstacle in passing through the wall."

"Indeed," replied the Assistant. "The element is extremely subtle; adhering to our nature, it acquires a renewed dynamic character."

"What if the medium himself were the object of the apportation? Would he be able to pass through the wall under the same circumstances?"

"Undoubtedly, as long as he remained under our control and closely connected to our energies. There are technicians here who are skilled enough to dematerialize the physical elements and reconstruct them straight away, conscious of the responsibility they're undertaking."

And smiling, he added:

"You mustn't forget that the flowers passed through a masonry wall with such assistance. Likewise, if we found it useful, the medium could be apported outside just as easily. In any construction of the physical realm, the clusters of atoms are not solid fortresses, just as is the case in our own sphere of action. There is empty space in all formations and through it the elements interpenetrate. The day will come when earthly science will be able to reintegrate the units and constitutions of atoms with the same assurance with which they are learning to disintegrate them."

Immediately thereafter, our fellow spirit workers, always interested in awakening their incarnate brothers and sisters to the realities of the spirit, reconnected the medium to his physical body.

The young man rubbed his face, half-asleep; however, as a result of calming passes, he lapsed back into a deep hypnotic state.

Revitalized and abundant ectoplasmic energies once more flowed from his nose and ears.

Followed by us, some of our colleagues went into the adjoining room,

There, on a small electric stove, a large pail of molten paraffin grabbed our attention.

A spirit with a friendly demeanor covered his right hand with the malleable paste flowing abundantly from the medium and materialized his hand to perfection. He then immersed it in the superheated paraffin and left the precious mold of his hand as a memento for the meeting's participants.

A young woman greeted us cordially and also worked the ectoplasm. She shaped three flowers, submerged them in the pail, and then laid them on the table for the participants as a kindly remembrance of that evening of tolerance and warmth.

Other spirits, friends of the place, brought in several seashells, which emanated delicate fragrances that spread throughout the room in subtle waves.

Noting that the spirit workers submitted the medium to complex magnetic procedures through which the materializing substance was returned to the physical body completely purified, we showered Aulus with lots of questions.

Do all incarnates actually possess the energy we were examining? Could we expect more manifestations of it in the future? Would this energy invariably have to be directed or could it organize itself in certain circumstances?

Aulus left the closing phase of the endeavor to the other workers, and explained:

"Ectoplasm is situated between dense and perispiritual matter; it is a product of the emanations of the soul through the filter of the body. It is a resource characteristic not only of human beings, but of all forms in nature. In certain special physiological organisms of the human race, it appears in greater amounts and in relative maturity for the manifestation needed for the physical effects we have analyzed. It is an amorphous element, but of great power and vitality. It can be compared to a genuine protoplasmic mass; it is extremely sensitive and animated by creative principles that function as conductors of electricity and magnetism. These principles are invariably subordinated to the thought and will of the medium who exteriorizes them, or the discarnate – or not – spirits who are attuned to the medium's mind, controlling his or her behavior. Infinitely pliable, it gives partial or complete form to the spirits who make themselves visible to the human eye or the camera; it gives consistency to wires, sticks and other types of visible or invisible devices in the phenomena of levitation; and it substantiates the images created by the medium's imagination, or the imagination of those who, mentally attuned, assist him or her. Thus, it demands a lot of attention and care on our part to keep it from being dominated by dark Intelligences, since falling into the hands and being manipulated by spirits still captive to debased passions could cause serious disturbance."

And indicating the medium, who was waking up, drowsy, he continued:

"By polarizing the energies from our plane, the medium functions as a maternal entity, from whose creative potential completely or partially materialized spirits draw the resources they need for their manifestations. In this way, they become his true offspring for a very short time."

Taking in this concept, Hilario said enthusiastically:

"That would mean that in the generating forces exuded by the medium and by the coworkers from our sphere, we could also find the fundamental principles of human genetics in configurations that earthly science is not yet aware of..."

"Yes, without question," confirmed the Assistant. "The principles are the same, although the aspects are different. The future reserves wonderful achievements in that regard. Let's continue to work and study."

The time we had available had ended. Aulus ended the remarkable conversation and invited us to leave.

29
Annotations about the Work

On the way back to Aulus's home, it occurred to me to ask his opinion with respect to various problems that always seem to surround those who dedicate themselves to the study of mediumistic matters.

While with the Assistant, we had briefly but surely touched on gripping material that had provided us with an excellent course of study.

Amid both incarnates and discarnates, we had closely examined the assimilation of mental currents, psychophony, possession, the out-of-body experience, clairvoyance, clairaudience, healing forces, telepathy, psychometry and materialization, in addition to a few of the crucially important themes of mediumship, such as the power of prayer, mental fixation, immersion of the subconscious, lycanthropy, obsession, fascination, the law of cause and effect, the out-of-body experience on the death bed, and corrupted energies – all without having to resort to terminological complexities.

In spite of our respect for human science, we wondered why it used such confusing terminology for occurrences common to everybody, when simplification would be much more interesting. For example, metapsychics called cryptic, hidden sensitivity "cryptestesia" and labeled the knowledge of facts without the aid of the physical senses as "metagnomia" ... They divided mediums (*sujets* in the vocabulary of some investigators) into two categories: those with "unusual psychological faculties" and those with "mechanical-physical-chemical faculties", and so on and so forth.

Why not simplify such difficulties of expression? After all – I thought – in essence, mediumship involves the interest of all humankind.

I was mulling over such thoughts when Aulus, obviously making note of my criticisms, considered:

"Mediumship undoubtedly is everyone's common heritage; however, each individual and each group make note of it in their own way. On our part, we can treat mediumship with evangelical simplicity, based on the clear teachings of the Master, who was in constant contact with powers invisible to the common person as he healed the obsessed and the sick, conversed with the great teachers who materialized on Mt. Tabor, listened to heavenly messengers in Gethsemane, and then returned in person to communicate with his disciples after his death on the cross. Earthly science, for now, cannot analyze it without the rigors of experimentation."

After a brief pause, he continued:

"It doesn't matter if aspects of the truth receive different names according to the inclination of the researchers. What does matter is the sincerity with which we devote ourselves to the good. The industrious effort of science is as sacred as the heroism of faith. Science, with its scales and test tubes, also exists to serve the Lord. By investigating and categorizing mediumistic phenomena, it will finally register psychic vibrations, thus ensuring the dignity of Religion in the New Age."

I didn't want to place the discussion in scientific realms, however. Our learning experience was drawing to a close. This was the last night we would be enjoying the wise company of our instructor and I wanted to hear what he had to say about mediumship per se.

For this reason, I directed our conversation, which resulted in the following dialogue:

"It is understandable that science does not examine the mediumistic field from our perspective. Logic and positive experimentation travel roads quite different from those of intuition. However, even in the currents of Spiritualism themselves, we see mediumship suffering the most diverse interpretations."

"What are you trying to say, Andre?"

"I'm referring to those brothers and sisters who accuse mediums of insanity and madness, recommending the segregating of the students of truth in temples of initiation, at a good distance from the legions of earth's sufferers and unlearned."

"Ah, yes! The sanctuary of religious initiation – whatever it may be – is valuable to us as an advanced outpost for the distribution of spiritual light. However, those who forget the law of cooperation in such sanctuaries isolate themselves in the ivory tower of their own pride, focusing on brilliant yet barren discussions. Such individuals are like travelers huddled together on a dangerous island of repose while the brave sailors of the good sweat and suffer to discover secure routes to the continent of fraternity and peace. The former rest in the shade of the trees, comforted by abundant game and fresh water as they study the grandeur of the sky or philosophize without benefit. But the day always comes when the furious tide overruns their makeshift home, pulling them out to sea for the resumption of their necessary experiences."

"Many scholars from our sphere of endeavor assert that only contact with higher order spirits should be cultivated, relegating ordinary mediumistic manifestations to the cesspool of obsession and infirmity, which, in their opinion, should be left alone without any attention on our part."

"That is complacency in the guise of wisdom. We cannot deny the fact that obsession is a mental disease, but could Medicine heal someone by neglecting to fulfill its duties? True, high order spirits from our plane never forsake the suffering and the small. Just as the sun shines on the palace as well as the cave with the same silent devotion, they help everybody in the name of Providence."

"There are many Spiritualists who do not tolerate any rudimentary manifestations in the area of mediumship. If the medium doesn't correspond to their demands, if he or she displays limited understanding or competence, they walk away, exasperated, labeling valuable expressions of phenomenology as fraudulent or deceitful."

Aulus smiled and replied:

"They are probably champions of least effort. They ignore the fact that the scholar was illiterate at the beginning of his or her life, and they probably condemn the child that still cannot read. These individuals, Andre, have forgotten the help they received in grade school; asking for easy ways – like the addict that demands drugs – they accustom themselves to deplorable attitudes towards life. They demand everything for themselves but disregard the obligation to assist those who are still behind."

"There are those who say that Spiritism proceeds wrongly in helping the unbalanced and the ill, because in doing so, it gives the impression of a Doctrine which, by force of mingling with the insane to give them assistance, converts its centers of prayer into vast asylums for the mentally alienated."

"That is plain foolishness on the part of those who avoid serving their neighbor. Medicine suffers no impairment by offering help to the sick. Honored by the hospitals where it is practiced, it becomes more praiseworthy the more it expands its assistance to the infirm. Spiritism cannot be held responsible for the mentally imbalanced who seek its help any more than doctors can be blamed for the sicknesses that require their intervention. As a matter of fact, Spiritism benefits tormented mediumship and the sick mind because it provides them with the balm and enlightenment necessary for their readjustment. It is very easy to contrive theories that exonerate us from our duty to serve others, but it is very hard to apply the lofty principles we espouse by employing our minds and our own hands. If the world's and our own recovery were limited to pretty words, Christ – our daily standard – would not have had to come to the needy. It would have been enough for him to have sent angelic proclamations to humankind without having to experience its ignorance and problems first hand. Fortunately, however, conscientious and sensible spiritualists are learning that our aim is to revive the Gospel on its pure and simple foundation, and that the Lord has not given us the treasure of faith only so that we can believe and speak, but also be ready to spread the good, beginning with ourselves."

"There are also those who state that, in every case of obsession, the law of cause and effect works implacably, and therefore there should not be any intervention on behalf of tormented mediumship."

"A mere argument of well-fed selfishness. That would be the same as forsaking the sick under the pretext that they are debtors before the Law. We all have to struggle to pay off our past debts, knowing that there is no unjustified suffering. And if we know that only pure love and constant service can ensure our redemption with regard to one another, then how can we disdain, in the name of the principles to which we ourselves are subjected, those who suffer? Today, it is the neighbor who suffers the consequences of certain actions in the past; tomorrow, it will be we ourselves who reap the results of gestures that dishonored our past and now afflict us in the present. If cooperation is lacking among victims on the thorn-covered road, surely the task of salvation will be much longer and difficult for each of us."

"Likewise, there is no lack of those who believe that we shouldn't concern ourselves with problems related to complex mediumship, because – they say – each person has to find the truth for him or herself. They believe that religion is nothing but a crutch and that no one should seek out instructors on matters of their own competence."

Aulus made a good-humored gesture and replied:

"That would be like eliminating the school and reviling the love that is inherent in All Creation. Any dignified religion – whatever the holy place where it is expressed – is a sanctuary for the education of the soul during its gradual evolution towards immortality. Let's imagine a large country, where millions of children have been relegated to moral and cultural abandonment by their parents and teachers under the allegation that it is the children's duty to seek virtue and wisdom by themselves ... Let's imagine a large field teeming with sick people, to whom eminent doctors would recommend they seek health by themselves, leaving them to their own devices ... Where would be the logic in such measures? Interdependence lies at the base of all the phenomena of life. The strong are the tutors of the weak. The learned are responsible for the unlearned. Children can't go without the help of their parents."

The Assistant paused briefly and proceeded:

"We have to remember that not everyone is of the same spiritual age, and that earthly humanity as a whole is still as far from angelhood as aggressive animality is from full human reasoning. It is way too soon for human beings to claim the right to plead for the Absolute Truth ... For now, it is essential that they work intensely, with ardent and profound devotion to the good in order to attain a broader understanding of the fragmentary or provisory realities of physical life. Looking at the matter from that point of view, we may be certain that the lack of schools for the spirit, or the suppression of instructors would cause an increase in the number of asylums and the relaxation of morals, because without the call to the dignifying of the individual through a process of mental growth and sublimation over time, we could count only on stagnation at the lower levels of life."

We were nearing the end of our trip.

The sanctuary-home where our Assistant resided was now in sight.

"Let us work cheerfully," Aulus said. "Time plus service to the good is the foundation for our victory."

Aulus was to leave for a lofty mission far away the following day. Thus, he promised us a farewell embrace the next morning.

30
Closing Pages

We followed the Assistant, now pondering our imminent separation...

Hilario and I were emotional and preoccupied.

At the rising of the sun, the field on the physical realm shone in the full light of morning.

Quiet and expectant, we approached a farmer clearing the soil with a hoe. Aulus pointed at him with his right hand and broke the silence:

"Look! Mediumship as an instrument of life appears everywhere. The farmer is the medium for the harvest, the plant is the medium for the fructification, and the flower is the medium for the fragrance. Everywhere, we give and receive, filtering the resources that surround us and molding their manifestation according to our abilities."

We continued on and soon we came to a simple carpenter's shop.

The Assistant pointed out the worker who was smoothing a large piece of wood and remarked:

"In the artisan we have a medium for valuable, useful things. From the devotion that he or she dedicates to the task, a lot of the comforts that civilization enjoys are born."

A little farther, we reached a small marble shop. In its doorway, a young man was using a chisel to shape the stone.

"That sculptor," said Aulus "is the medium for a masterpiece. Art is the mediumship for Beauty, in which we find sublime visions of the future reserved for us."

The Assistant was continuing his important considerations on the subject, when we passed by some cleanup workers removing trash from a large plaza.

"Street sweepers," he said respectfully, "valiant mediums for cleanliness."

Soon thereafter we came to a building housing a court of justice, and the Assistant remarked:

"This is a court where the judge is the medium for the law. All individuals, in their activities, professions and associations, are instruments of the forces to which they devote themselves. They produce in accordance with the superior or inferior ideals that inspire them, attracting the invisible elements that surround them according to the nature of the sentiments and ideas they nurture themselves with."

We finally arrived at the home where Hilario and I would dedicate ourselves to helping a sick child.

At this point of the journey, the Instructor, expected some distance from there, would finally take his leave from us.

Aulus followed us paternally inside the home. An older gentleman and his wife were having breakfast with their three small children.

Next to a clean and frugal table, the weary and pale child who would receive our help was resting in a large chair.

The Instructor gazed at the touching scene, stating:

"Family represents a meeting of souls in the process of evolution, readjustment, spiritual growth or sanctification. Man and woman, embracing marriage as a school of love and work to honor the commitments they assumed before the Universal Harmony, transform themselves into mediums for life itself, taking responsibility for the materialization of former friends and enemies who become their sons and daughters in the domestic sanctuary. Lived out with dignity, fatherhood and motherhood are callings of the highest level for the reincarnate spirit, because, through them, regeneration and progress are effectuated with security and clarity. Beyond the home, it would be difficult to identify a place where mediumship is more spontaneous and pure, since in the position of fathers and mothers, men and women truly deserving of these titles learn to seek their own sublimation through sacrifice on behalf of the souls who manifest through them as children."

And in a moment of lovely inspiration, he concluded:

"The physical family can be compared to a meeting of spiritual service in space and time, sculpting hearts for immortality."

The mentor then looked at the clock and remarked:

"Those who journey with responsibilities must not forget the time."

He left hurriedly and we followed him to a nearby plaza.

Aulus gazed up at the blue sky, where the sun seemed as if it were diffusing itself in a shower of quintessential gold. He was about to embrace us when he perceived my most innermost wish. He said humbly:

"Say a prayer for us, Andre!"

Reverently, I prayed aloud:

"Lord Jesus!
Make us worthy of those who spread truth and love!

Add the treasures of wisdom to the souls who become great by assisting their fellow beings.

Help those who deny themselves, distributing hope and peace in Your Name…

Teach us how to honor your faithful disciples with the respect and love we owe them.

Uproot the harmful weeds of indiscipline and pride from the field of our souls so that simplicity may favor our renewal.

Do not leave us to our own blindness, but guide our steps towards those who evolve by humbling themselves, and who, by being noble and great in your eyes, do not feel lessened by making themselves small in order to help us…

Glorify them, Lord, crowning their heads with your laurels of light!"

The Assistant must have realized that for us he personified those benefactors whose greatness I had evoked. However, I had not dared to pronounce his name, such was the veneration he deserved from us.

After my prayer, I looked at him with tear-filled eyes.

Aulus didn't say a word.

Covered in luminescent radiance, letting us know that he too was saying farewell to us in prayer, he held us both in one embrace and left…

Like children, Hilario and I, in mute tears of gratitude, watched him until he vanished in the distance.

Remembering the task that awaited us and praising the work that everywhere was our blessing, we proceeded to assist the sick child, like someone joining the great future…